LABORATORY MANUAL
OF
PHYSICAL CHEMISTRY

LABORATORY MANUAL

OF

PHYSICAL CHEMISTRY

BY

ALBERT W. DAVISON
Professor of Chemical Engineering

AND

HENRY S. van KLOOSTER
Professor of Physical Chemistry
Rensselaer Polytechnic Institute

SECOND EDITION

REVISED AND ENLARGED

NEW YORK

JOHN WILEY & SONS, Inc.

London: CHAPMAN & HALL, Limited

1931

PRINTED IN U. S. A.

PRESS OF
BRAUNWORTH & CO., INC.
BOOK MANUFACTURERS
BROOKLYN, NEW YORK

PREFACE TO SECOND EDITION

In preparing this second edition of their Laboratory Manual, the authors have been guided by the experience accumulated during the nine years which have elapsed since the first appearance of the Manual. Directions for performance of the experiments have been clarified and simplified. The apparatus needed to carry out the various numbers has, wherever possible, been made to conform to types which are commercially available.

A short theoretical discussion of the principles involved in each experiment has been included in the body of the text, and such formulæ as are necessary in making the various calculations are presented.

The number of exercises has been extended to forty. The new experiments are all quantitative in character. Additional tables required for some new experiments have been added to the Appendix.

THE AUTHORS.

TROY, NEW YORK,
January, 1931.

v

<u>Finished</u>   To do

\# 1   47
   2   48
   3   24
   5   32
   7   33
  10   35
  15   37
  18   38
  21 ✓   39
  16   40
  22 a✓   20

CONTENTS

PAGE

PREFACE TO SECOND EDITION... v

LIST OF REFERENCES... ix

1. Determination of vapor density. Dumas' method.................. 1

2. Determination of vapor density. Victor Meyer's method......... 5

3. Graham's effusion law; densities of gases..................... 11

4. Vapor pressure of liquids.................................... 15

5. Surface tension and association factor of liquids............ 20

6. Measurement of surface tension. Drop-weight method.......... 24

7. Viscosity.. 29

8. Refractive index, density and molecular refractivity of liquids.......... 34

9. Solubility. The van't Hoff isochore......................... 40

10. Lowering of the freezing point. Beckmann method............. 44

11. Lowering of the freezing point. Dewar vacuum-flask method....... 50

12. Elevation of the boiling point. The Cottrell apparatus....... 58

13. Elevation of the boiling point. The Eykman method........... 63

14. Vapor pressure lowering by a dissolved substance. Raoult's law........ 70

15. Distillation with steam...................................... 75

16. Distribution of a substance between two non-miscible liquids.......... 80

17. Boiling points of binary systems (minimum boiling liquids)........... 84

18. Boiling points of binary systems. Siwoloboff's method........... 90

19. Boiling point and vapor composition curve................... 94

20. Partially miscible liquids. Determination of mutual solubility........ 100

21. Solubility curve for a ternary system of liquids............. 104

22. Transition points in the solid state........................ 109

23. Phase diagram for a two-component system of metals......... 117

24. Monomolecular reaction: decomposition of hydrogen peroxide........ 123

25. Monomolecular reaction: inversion of cane sugar............ 128

26. Bimolecular reaction: sodium thiosulphate+ethyl bromacetate........ 134

27. Bimolecular reaction: saponification of ethyl acetate....... 139

28. Heat of neutralization...................................... 144

29. Heat of combustion... 151

	PAGE
30. Heat of solution...	160
31. Heat of vaporization. Trouton's law......................	167
32. Adsorption from solution...................................	171
33. Flocculation of suspensoids by electrolytes..............	175
34. Solubility product..	179
35. Conductivity and degree of ionization....................	184
36. Hydrolysis. Conductivity method.........................	191
37. Transport numbers..	195
38. Electromotive force measurements: concentration cells...	201
39. Hydrogen ion concentration: electrometric titration.....	207
40. Indicators, buffer solutions, hydrolysis.................	217
TABLES, 1–17...	225

LIST OF REFERENCES

A. *Textbooks*:

BELL AND GROSS:	Elements of Physical Chemistry, Longmans, Green and Co., New York (1929).
BIGELOW:	Theoretical and Physical Chemistry, The Century Co., New York (1914).
CARTLEDGE:	Introductory Theoretical Chemistry, Ginn and Co., New York (1929).
CREIGHTON–FINK:	Principles and Applications of Electrochemistry, Vol. I, Principles, 2nd Ed., John Wiley & Sons, New York (1930).
CROCKER AND MATTHEWS:	Theoretical and Experimental Physical Chemistry, Macmillan Co., New York (1928).
EUCKEN, JETTE AND LA MER:	Fundamentals of Physical Chemistry, McGraw–Hill Book Co., New York (1925).
GETMAN:	Outlines of Theoretical Chemistry, 5th Ed., John Wiley & Sons, New York (1931).
JONES:	Elements of Physical Chemistry, 4th Ed., Macmillan Co., New York (1915).
LINCOLN:	Textbook of Physical Chemistry, Rev. Ed., D. C. Heath and Co., New York (1920).
LOWRY AND SUGDEN:	Class Book of Physical Chemistry, Macmillan Co., New York (1929).
MILLARD:	Physical Chemistry for Colleges, 2nd Ed., McGraw–Hill Book Co., New York (1926).
MORGAN:	Elements of Physical Chemistry, 5th Ed., John Wiley & Sons, New York (1923).
NERNST (CODD):	Theoretical Chemistry from the Standpoint of Avogadro's Rule, 5th Ed., Macmillan Co., New York (1923).
NOYES AND SHERRILL:	Chemical Principles, Macmillan Co., New York (1922).
SENTER:	Outlines of Physical Chemistry, 14th Ed., Van Nostrand Co., New York (1926).

TAYLOR:	Elementary Physical Chemistry, Van Nostrand Co., New York (1927).
WALKER:	Introduction to Physical Chemistry, 9th Ed., Macmillan Co., New York (1922).
WASHBURN:	Principles of Physical Chemistry, 2nd Ed., McGraw–Hill Book Co., New York (1921).

B. *Laboratory Manuals*:

BILTZ (JONES–KING):	Practical Methods of Determining Molecular Weights, Chemical Publishing Co., Easton, Pa. (1899).
BRIGGS:	Laboratory Outlines in Physical Chemistry, Ithaca, N. Y. (1920).
DANIELS, MATHEWS AND WILLIAMS:	Experimental Physical Chemistry, McGraw–Hill Book Co., New York (1929).
EWELL:	Physical Chemistry, Theory and Practice, Blakiston, Philadelphia (1909).
FINDLAY:	Practical Physical Chemistry, 4th Ed., Longmans, Green and Co., New York (1923).
FIRTH:	Practical Physical Chemistry, Van Nostrand Co., New York (1916).
GETMAN:	Laboratory Exercises in Physical Chemistry, 2nd Ed., John Wiley & Sons, New York (1908).
GRAY:	Manual of Practical Physical Chemistry, Macmillan Co., New York (1914).
VAN KLOOSTER:	Lecture and Laboratory Experiments in Physical Chemistry, Chemical Publishing Co., Easton, Pa. (1925).
MACK AND FRANCE:	Laboratory Manual of Elementary Physical Chemistry, Van Nostrand Co., New York (1928).
PRING:	Laboratory Exercises in Physical Chemistry, University Press, Manchester (1911).
REILLY, RAE AND WHEELER:	Physico-chemical Methods, Van Nostrand Co., New York (1926).
ROTH (CAMERON):	Exercises in Physical Chemistry, Van Nostrand Co., New York (1920).
SHERRILL:	Laboratory Experiments on Physico-chemical Principles, Macmillan Co., New York (1923).
TRAUBE (HARDIN):	Physico-chemical Methods, Blakiston, Philadelphia (1898).

C. *Special Texts and Reference Books*:

ALEXANDER:	Colloid Chemistry, Theoretical and Applied, 3 vols., New York (1926–28).
ALLMAND–ELLINGHAM:	Principles of Applied Electrochemistry, 2nd Ed., New York (1924).
BINGHAM:	Fluidity and Plasticity, New York (1922).
CLARK:	Determination of Hydrogen Ions, 3rd Ed., Baltimore (1928).
DANIELS:	Mathematical Preparation for Physical Chemistry, New York (1928).
FINDLAY:	The Phase Rule, 6th Ed., New York (1927).
KRUYT (VAN KLOOSTER):	Colloids, 2nd Ed., New York (1930).
LATIMER–HILDEBRAND:	Reference book, New York (1929).
LEWIS:	System of Physical Chemistry, 3 vols., New York (1924–25).
RIDEAL:	Introduction to Surface Chemistry, New York (1927).
ROBINSON:	Elements of Fractional Distillation, 2nd Ed., New York (1928).
TAYLOR:	Treatise on Physical Chemistry, 2nd Ed., 2 vols., New York (1931).
YOUNG:	Distillation Principles and Processes, London (1922).

D. *Tables of Constants:*

International Critical Tables, Vols. I–VI.

International Research Council's Annual Tables, Vols. I–VII.

Landolt-Börnstein's Physico-Chemical Tables, Vols. I and II (1923). Suppl. 1 (1927).

Olsen: Van Nostrand's Chemical Annual (1927).

LABORATORY MANUAL OF PHYSICAL CHEMISTRY

EXPERIMENT 1

DETERMINATION OF VAPOR DENSITY— DUMAS' METHOD

Object:

To determine the vapor density and the molecular weight in the vapor state, of an assigned liquid.

Discussion:

In this method, the vapor density is determined by direct weighing. A glass bulb of approximately 250-c.c. capacity is accurately weighed when filled with air, when filled with the vapor to be investigated, and when filled with water. By noting the temperatures and pressures at which the bulb was filled with these respective substances, it is possible to calculate (a) the volume of the bulb, (b) the weight of air contained by the bulb when first weighed, (c) the weight of the "empty" bulb and (d) the density of the vapor.

For determinations of the highest accuracy, all weights should be reduced to ".in vacuo." For ordinary work, however, this refinement is quite unnecessary.

Apparatus and Chemicals required:

Dumas' vapor density apparatus, 2 Bunsen burners, barometer, thermometer (0–110° C.), 500-c.c. beaker, file, crucible tongs.

Volatile liquids, such as absolute alcohol, ether, carbon disulfide, carbon tetrachloride, for investigation.

Method of Procedure:

Thoroughly clean and dry the Dumas bulb, and draw the tip out to a fine capillary. Weigh the bulb accurately, noting the temperature of the balance case, and the barometric pressure. Record the values as W_1, t_1 and p_1.

Place about 10 c.c. of the liquid assigned for the investigation in the bulb. This is most readily done by warming the bulb slightly, and immersing the tip beneath the surface of the liquid. As the bulb cools, liquid will be drawn up into it.

Now clamp the bulb in the vaporizing bath in such a manner that only the tip projects above the surface. For liquids boiling below 90°, boiling water is satisfactory for the bath. For liquids boiling above 90°, oil may be used. In the latter case, it is essential that the temperature of the oil be held at least 10° above the boiling point of the liquid being investigated.

When the liquid within the bulb has completely vaporized, seal off the tip; record the temperature of the bath, and the barometric pressure as t_2 and p_2.

Allow the bulb to cool, clean and dry it, and weigh. Record as W_2.

Prepare about 500 c.c. of gas-free water by boiling distilled water, and cooling it to room temperature. Fill the bulb with this water by breaking off the tip, while immersed in the water. The bulb should fill completely. If it does not, consult the instructor. Record the temperature of the water as t_3.

Dry the outside of the bulb, and weigh it, with the tip (filled with water) which was cut off, to the nearest centigram on the large balance. Record as W_3.

Observations and Measurements:

Sample investigated............................. *C Cl₄*

Weight of bulb full of air (W_1)................ *92.705* g.

Temperature of balance case (t_1)............. *34.87*

Observed barometric pressure p_1.............

........corrected..................... *346.87*

Weight of bulb full of vapor (W_2).............. g.

Temperature of bath at time of sealing (t_2).......
Barometric pressure at time of sealing (p_2).......
.........corrected.........................
Weight of bulb filled with water (W_3)............ — g.
Temperature of water used for filling (t_3).. ......

Calculations:

$W_3 - W_1$ gives the apparent mass (m_1) of water contained in the bulb. This, divided by the density of water at temperature t_3, gives the apparent volume of the bulb (V_b) in c.c. The true mass of water contained in the bulb is greater than the apparent mass, by the weight of the air contained in the bulb when W_1 was taken. One cubic centimeter of air (s.c.) weighs 0.001293 gm.

1. Calculate the weight of 1 c.c. of air at t_1 and p_1, and multiply this value by V_b, to obtain the correction which is to be added to m_1 in order to find the true mass of water m. Then m, divided by the density of water at t_3, gives the true volume of the bulb at t_3. Call this V_3.

2. Calculate the exact mass of air contained in the bulb, by multiplying V_3 by the weight of 1 c.c. of air at t_1 and p_1. Call this m_a. Then $W_1 - m_a$ gives the mass of the empty bulb, and $W_2 - (W_1 - m_a)$ gives the true mass of the vapor in the bulb, mv. Since the bulb was filled at an elevated temperature, the volume V_3 does not represent the true volume of the vapor. V_3 must be increased to $V_3 + V_3(0.000025)(t_2 - t)_1$, where 0.000025 is the cubical coefficient of expansion of glass. Call this new volume V_4.

3. Having found the mass of vapor, its true volume, temperature, and pressure, calculate the vapor density.

4. Compute the molecular weight.

over

W_1 (flask in air)   96.225 gr.

W_2 (flask + vapor)   97.705 gr.

W_3 (Wt of V at room T)   346.87 gr.

V (volume)   347.6 cc

d_1 (density of air at room T)   .997 9

d_2 (H_2O at room T)   25.3°

T = absolute T. of boil. H_2O 373.°

Barometric reading   761.2

M. 119.5 for CCl_4

$$V d_3 = W_3 = (347.6 \times .9979) = 346.87$$

$$V_0 = \frac{273 \times 761.2 \times 347.6}{760 (273 + 100)} = 348.19$$

$$d_2 = d_1 + \frac{W_2 - W_1}{V} = .001184 + \frac{97.705 - 96.225}{347.6} = .005344$$

$$M = \frac{22400 \, d_2 \, V}{V_0} = 119.5$$

EXPERIMENT 2

DETERMINATION OF VAPOR DENSITY— VICTOR MEYER'S METHOD

Object:

To determine vapor density and molecular weight by the Victor Meyer method.[1]

Discussion:

A weighed quantity of the liquid under investigation is caused to evaporate in a heated tube, which is fitted with a delivery arm. As vapor is formed, an equivalent volume of air is displaced from the vaporization tube, and is collected in an eudiometer.

At the close of the experiment, the volume, temperature, and pressure of the displaced air, and the height of the meniscus above the level of water in the pneumatic trough, are noted. From these data, the volume of the vapor is calculated for standard conditions.

In collecting air over water, the volume under standard conditions is given by the following equation:

$$V_s = V \times \frac{273}{273 + t} \times \frac{p - h/13.6 - w}{760}$$

where: V is the observed volume,

t the temperature of the water, which should be the same as that of the room,

---

[1] The standard Victor Meyer apparatus, or Weiser's modification (Jour. Phys. Chem., **20**, 532, 1916), may be used with equal facility. The description in the text, and Fig. 2 apply to Weiser's modification. When using the standard Victor Meyer apparatus, the same directions apply.

h the height of the meniscus in millimeters,

w the vapor pressure of the water at room temperature,

and p the corrected barometric pressure.

The weight of the liquid used, divided by the volume of the vapor in liters, gives the standard density. The molecular weight is obtained by multiplying this density by 22.4.

Apparatus and Chemicals required:

Victor Meyer Apparatus (see Fig. 1) or Weiser's modification of the same (see Fig. 2), 2 iron stands, 3 rings, clamp, Bunsen burner, wire gauze, eudiometer, pneumatic trough, thermometer (0–100°) pumice, glass beads, glass wool or cotton, glass stoppered vials (0.2–0.55 contents), volatile liquids for investigation.

The assembled apparatus is shown in Fig. 2. The inner vaporization tube is securely held in place within the outer jacket by means of a cork split vertically with holes to fit the inlet- and exit-tube of the apparatus and the bent glass tube for the escape of the steam. The two portions of the cork are fastened firmly together by means of a wire around the top.

Method of Procedure:

Fill the bulb of the jacket two-thirds full of water and support the jacket on a wire gauze in a quiet place free from air currents.

Place the inner tube in position and fasten it securely by means of the cork. Fill the dish which serves as pneumatic trough with water and let the end of the capillary delivery tube dip beneath the surface of the water. Fill the graduated eudiometer tube with water, invert it, and clamp it near the delivery tube in such a way that it can be quickly moved over the tip.

Heat the jacket with a low flame and as soon as the water begins to boil, adjust the height of the flame in such a manner that steam just escapes from the bent glass tube.

Weigh about 0.1 gram of the assigned liquid into the small glass stoppered vial and stopper tightly.

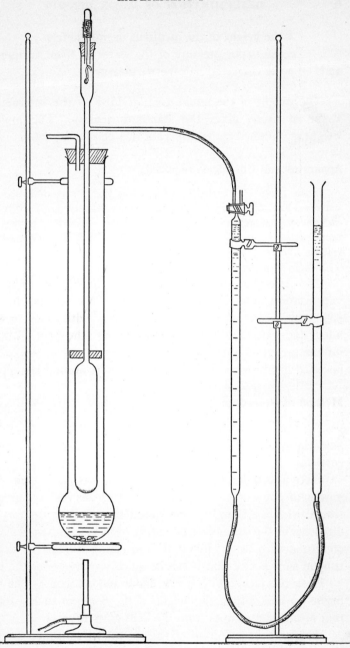

Fig. 1.

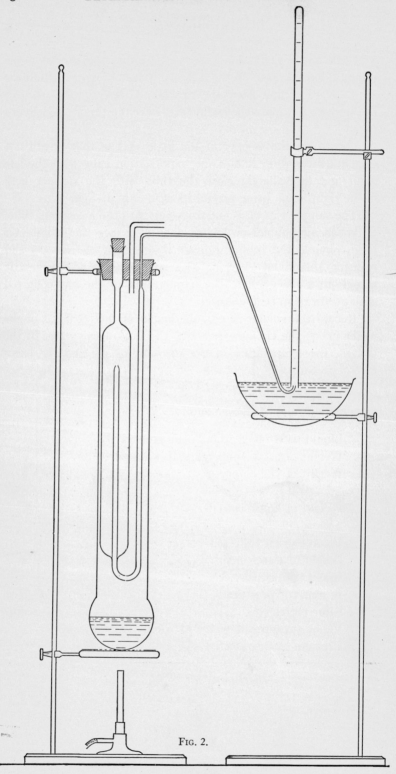

FIG. 2.

Close the vaporization tube by a rubber stopper and continue to boil the water in the jacket. When no more air bubbles are seen to escape from the capillary delivery tube, remove the stopper and place the eudiometer over the tip of the delivery tube.

Loosen up the stopper of the little vial so that it will not stick later on, drop it into the vaporization tube with the left hand and immediately close the tube with the stopper held in the right hand, being careful to secure an air-tight joint.

The sample vaporizes and drives air into the measuring tube.

When air bubbles no longer come over into the eudiometer tube, remove the rubber stopper again, turn off the gas and transfer the stand carrying the eudiometer and pneumatic trough to a place where the temperature of the gas collected may attain room temperature.

Record the volume of gas, the height of the meniscus of the water inside the eudiometer above the level of the water in the trough, the temperature of the surrounding air and the barometric pressure.

Observations and Measurements:

Liquid used taken from bottle labeled. . . . . CCl_4

Weight of glass stoppered vial + liquid. . . . . .9102 g.

Weight of vial empty. . . . . .7041 g.

Weight of liquid used. . . . . .2061 g.

Volume of air collected. 33 c.c.

Height of water meniscus. . . . . — mm.

Room temperature. . . . . 21.0 C.

Barometric pressure. . . . . 756 mm.

Same corrected. . . . . — mm.

Vapor pressure of water at room temperature.[1]

Pressure of air collected. — mm.

[1] Consult Table 1, Appendix.

$$\frac{Wt\ of\ sample \times (t\ of\ H_2O + 273.1)\ 760 \times 22400}{Bar.\ P. -)\ vol\ of\ air + 273.1} = M.$$

Calculations:

From the weight of the liquid, the volume, the temperature and the pressure of the air collected calculate:

    1. The specific gravity of the vapor with respect to air.
    2. The density of the vapor under standard conditions.
    3. The molecular weight of the compound.

Weight of capsule - - - - - - - g

Weight of cap + CCl_4 - - - - - - - g.

Weight of CCl_4 (2-1)- - - - - - - - g

Temp of H_2O (cyl.) - - - - - - - - °

Vol of air. - - - - - - - - c c

Barometric read. - - - - - - - mm

$$\frac{.2061 \times 21.6 + 273.1 \times 760 \times 22400}{756 - \quad) \; 33.1 + 273.1}$$

EXPERIMENT 3

GRAHAM'S EFFUSION LAW; DENSITIES OF GASES

Object:

To apply Graham's effusion law to the determination of gas densities and molecular weights.

Discussion:

Graham in 1846 announced the principle that, when gases diffuse through small openings or porous walls, the rates at which they diffuse are inversely proportional to the square roots of their densities. Dealing with two gases, A and B, we are thus enabled to formulate the equation:

$$r_A : r_B = \sqrt{d_B} : \sqrt{d_A}$$

where r and d are, respectively, the rates of diffusion and densities.

If we are concerned with equal volumes of two gases, diffusing under identical conditions, it is obvious that rates will be inversely proportional to diffusion times:

$$r_A : r_B = t_B : t_A$$

Hence the times required for equal volumes of two gases to diffuse under identical conditions are directly proportional to the square roots of the densities of the gases

$$t_A : t_B = \sqrt{d_A} : \sqrt{d_B}$$

In applying this principle to the determination of the density of a given gas, the time required for a definite volume of gas to escape from the apparatus, under certain definite changing conditions, is compared with the time required for an equal volume of some standard gas, such as air, to escape under identical changing conditions. When air is taken as standard, its "specific gravity" is unity. The density of air is 1.293 gms. per liter.

Apparatus and Chemicals required:

Schilling's Specific Gravity Gas Apparatus, Stopwatch.
Tanks containing oxygen, hydrogen, nitrogen; illuminating gas.

The apparatus (Schilling's) is arranged as shown in Fig. 3. The effusion tube, held tightly at its upper end by means of a wood clamp, weighted by a lead disk, is submerged in the water to a certain depth which must not change in order that the average pressure under which the gases effuse remain the same throughout the whole experiment. The hole in the platinum foil through which the gases effuse must be exceedingly small. It is punched by means of a very fine needle and if necessary can be hammered down until a very small opening remains. The foil is cemented to the end of stopcock A by means of china cement or universal wax (a mixture of one part of venetian turpentine and four parts of bees-wax).

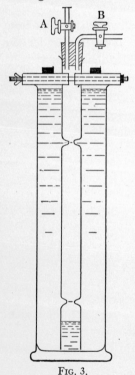

FIG. 3.

Method of Procedure:

Close stopcock A, open B and fill the effusion tube with air, either by blowing it in from the laboratory air lines or by lifting the tube out of the water.

Close B, replace the tube and see that the water in the outer cylinder rises to within an inch of the top.

See that the water in the apparatus is saturated each time with the gas under observation and that it has the temperature of the room.

With stopwatch in hand, open stopcock A and allow the air to pass through the opening in the foil. Start the watch when the rising water passes the mark on the lower constriction of the effusion tube and stop it when the water passes the mark on the upper constriction.

Fill the tube again with air and repeat the observation and continue until at least three determinations have been made which check to two-fifths of a second.

Open both stopcocks and pass hydrogen through the apparatus until all the air has been replaced by hydrogen, then close *A* and fill the tube with hydrogen, raising it if necessary to secure the entry of a sufficient amount of gas.

Close *B*, open *A* and record the time required for this gas to effuse through the opening. Repeat the operation until at least three good checks have been obtained.

Replace the residual hydrogen with illuminating gas from the laboratory fuel lines, performing the operation under the hood to prevent the escape of toxic gases into the room.

Operate as before and obtain at least three determinations which check to two-fifths of a second.

Record of Observations:

Gas used ..O........
Effusion time 49 2/5, 48 3/5, 50, 49.

Gas used ..air........
Effusion time 1.14 3/5, 1.15, ..., 75.

Gas used ..H........
Effusion time 41 1/5, 42 1/5, 40, ...

Gas used ....
Effusion time ...., ..., ..., ...

Calculation of Results:

1. By means of Graham's effusion law, calculate the specific gravity (air = 1) of each of the gases used.

2. From the specific gravities, calculate the density of each gas.

3. Calculate the molecular weight (for illuminating gas the "apparent" molecular weight).

$49 : 75 = \sqrt{x} : \sqrt{1}$

$\sqrt{x} = \frac{49}{75} = .653$

$x = .427$

EXPERIMENT 4

VAPOR PRESSURE OF LIQUIDS

Object:

To determine the vapor pressure curve for a liquid.

Discussion:

In using any dynamic method for determining the vapor pressure of a pure liquid or a solution, the vapor pressure of the liquid, confined in a closed system, is balanced by a manometer containing mercury or some other suitable fluid.

The isotensiscope [1] furnishes a ready means for ascertaining when the vapor pressure of the liquid is accurately balanced by the height (or depression) of the manometer. Its use is particularly recommended for pure liquids.

Apparatus and Chemicals required:

Isotensiscope, or an equivalent vapor pressure apparatus, 2-liter beaker, condenser, open U-tube-manometer (each arm 800 mm. long), iron stand, 3 clamps, Bunsen burner, electric hot plate, or electric immersion heater (preferred) for heating the bath, heavy 4-gallon bottle, 2 three-way stopcocks, suction pump, source of low pressure air (10 or 15 lb.), thermometer (0–110°), thermometer (0–250°), stirring apparatus, glass and rubber tubing.

The arrangement of the apparatus is readily understood from Fig. 4. The isotensiscope consists of a cylindrical bulb of about 25-c.c. capacity sealed to a 10-c.c. pipette bent as shown in Fig. 5 and connected to a reflux condenser by means of a ground-glass joint. The condenser communicates on the left

---

[1] Smith and Menzies, J.A.C.S., **32**, 1412 (1910); Derby and Yngve, *ibid.*, **38**, 1439 (1916); Edgar and Swan, *ibid.*, **44**, 570 (1922).

15

with the manometer, and on the right with a three-way stop-cock, one arm of which leads to the reservoir bottle, the other to the atmosphere. The reservoir bottle is connected through a three-way stopcock to a suction pump, and to the air line.

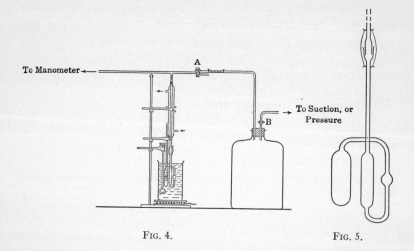

To Manometer

A

To Suction, or Pressure

B

FIG. 4.   FIG. 5.

Method of Procedure:

Clean and dry the isotensiscope, and assemble as shown in Fig. 4. Apply suction to the apparatus, close A, and see that there are no leaks. If the apparatus is tight, admit air through A, remove the bulb, and fill it about two-thirds full of the liquid to be investigated.

Re-assemble the apparatus, and fill the bath with water for temperatures up to 100°, or with oil or glycerol for higher temperatures. Turn stopcock A so that the system is open to the atmosphere, commence stirring, and heat the bath until the liquid in the tube commences to boil. After sufficient condensate has collected in the trap to seal it, continue the boiling long enough to expel all air from the space between the main body of the liquid and the trap, then carry the temperature up to the highest value at which it is desired to determine the vapor pressure.

By manipulating stopcocks *A* and *B*, admitting or removing air as needed, the liquid levels in the two arms of the trap are kept at the same height. *It is very important that air is not permitted to be sucked back into the bulb.*

When the heat is turned off, and as the system cools down, the liquid in the trap is kept level by manipulation of the two stopcocks. Simultaneous readings of the manometer and the thermometer are taken, and supply the necessary data for the vapor pressure curve. These readings may be taken for every one or two degrees fall in temperature.

Observations and Meausrements:

> Liquid investigated............
> Barometer at start............ Corrected............
> Barometer at end............. Corrected............

Temperature	Manometer reading	Vapor pressure
......	......	......
......	......	......
......	......	......
......	......	......
......	......	......
......	......	......
......	......	......
......	......	......
......	......	......
......	......	......
......	......	......
......	......	......

Calculations:

1. Plot the vapor pressure curve.

2. Plot, on the same sheet as 1, the vapor pressure curve for the same liquid from data given in the tables of constants quoted on p. xi, and compare your results with those given in the literature.

3. Calculate the (average) heat of vaporization over a small temperature interval, using the equation of Clapeyron–Clausius.

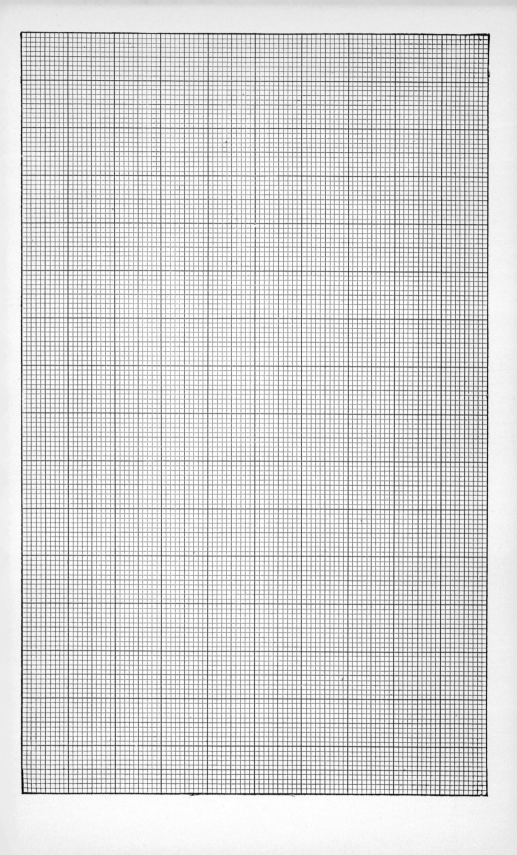

EXPERIMENT 5

SURFACE TENSION AND ASSOCIATION FACTOR OF LIQUIDS

Object:

To determine the surface tension, association factor, and critical temperature of an assigned liquid, by the capillary-rise method.

Discussion:

For water and many other liquids which readily wet glass, the surface tension may be measured by observing the height to which those liquids rise in capillary tubes. The equation used is the following:

$$\gamma = \tfrac{1}{2}hdgr \tag{1}$$

where: γ is the surface tension in dynes per centimeter (ergs per square centimeter),

h the capillary rise in centimeters,

r the radius of the tube in centimeters,

d the density of the liquid

and g the acceleration due to gravity.

Ramsay and Shields showed that the "surface energy" of a given liquid depends on its temperature and on the critical temperature as follows:

$$\gamma\left(\frac{M}{d}\right)^{2/3} = k(t_c - t - 6) \tag{2}$$

From Equation 2 it may easily be shown that the rate of change of surface energy with temperature is the constant k:

$$\frac{\gamma_1\left(\dfrac{M}{d_1}\right)^{2/3} - \gamma_2\left(\dfrac{M}{d_2}\right)^{2/3}}{t_2 - t_1} = k \tag{3}$$

20

If the liquid is unassociated, the value of k is 2.12; if associated, k comes out less than this value. For an associated liquid, the degree of association x is given by:

$$x = \left(\frac{2.12}{k}\right)^{3/2} \tag{4}$$

Apparatus and Chemicals required:

Iron stand, Bunsen burner, ring, clamp, tall 2-liter beaker, stirrer, thermometer, capillary tubes (stems of broken thermometers are excellent) or small-bore glass tubing which may be drawn to capillary size as needed. Cathetometer (or mm. scales), microscope fitted with ocular micrometer and stage micrometer, freezing-point tube.

Bottles containing water and other liquids to be investigated.

Method of Procedure:

For the capillary tubes, the student may use either small-bore thermometer stems or he may draw out his capillaries as they are needed. The latter procedure is to be preferred since freshly drawn tubes are clean.

It is very essential that the utmost care be observed in order to avoid grease films and other forms of contamination which will vitiate the results. If thermometer stems are used, they must be carefully cleaned with hot cleaning solution before use.

Assemble the apparatus as indicated in Fig. 6, placing the liquid to be investigated inside the freezing-point tube and water in the

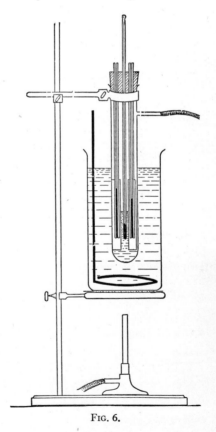

Fig. 6.

beaker which serves as a constant temperature bath. Bring the temperature to 20°. Blow gently into a rubber tube connected to the side arm of the apparatus in order to force the liquid up into the capillaries to a height greater than that of equilibrium. Then allow it to come to equilibrium.

Measure the height to which the liquid rises and note the exact point at which it stands in each capillary.

Remove the tubes from the apparatus, cut them off exactly at the point where the meniscus stood, and measure the diameter of each tube with the measuring microscope. At least three measurements should be made across diameters which intersect each other at 60°.

Assemble new tubes in the apparatus, raise the temperature to 40° and repeat the observations. Then make another set of observations at 60°.

Observations and Measurements:

	Tube 1	*Tube 2*
Liquid used.................	H₂O	C₆H₆
Capillary rise at 20°......	2.9	1.3
Diameter of tube...........		
Capillary rise at 40°......		
Diameter of tube...........		
Capillary rise at 60°......		
Diameter of tube...........		
Surface tension at 20°.....	72.8	31.69
40°.....		
60°.....		

Calculations: *See page 23.*

1. Calculate the surface tension for each temperature.

2. By means of Equation 3, calculate the rate of change of surface energy between 20° and 40° and between 40° and 60°.

3. From the two values of k thus obtained, calculate the association factor between 20° and 40° and between 40° and 60°.

4. From your best measurement of surface tension, calculate the critical temperature for the liquid, using Equation 2.

$$\frac{\alpha = h_1 d_1}{\alpha = h d} = \frac{72.8 \times 1.3 \times .8785}{2.9 \times 1.0} = 31.69$$

density of C_6H_6 = .8785 .   Westfall.

h_1 = 1.3

Surface T. H_2O = 72.8

h = 2.9

d of H_2O = 1.0

EXPERIMENT 6

MEASUREMENT OF SURFACE TENSION.
DROP-WEIGHT METHOD

Object:

To measure the surface tension by the drop-weight method.

Discussion:

The capillary-rise method of measuring surface tension described in the preceding experiment presents certain difficulties which render it unfit for work of the highest accuracy. Many years ago Tate showed that the following relation exists between the weight of an ideal drop falling from a specially prepared tip, and the surface tension:

$$W = mg = 2\pi r \gamma \qquad (1)$$

where: m is the mass of the drop,

g the acceleration due to gravity,

r the radius of the tip in centimeters,

and γ the surface tension in dynes.

Harkins [1] has shown that although the equation of Tate holds for an ideal drop, it requires a certain modification if it is to represent the true relation between the weight of a drop falling from a given tip, and the surface tension. Harkins has proposed the following modification of the Tate equation:

$$W = mg = 2\pi r \gamma F \qquad (2)$$

where F is a function of the radius of the tube, and the reciprocal of the cube root of the volume of the drop. Harkins has pre-

[1] Harkins and Brown, J.A.C.S., **41**, 499 (1919), *et al.*

24

pared tables of values for F, corresponding to various values of $\frac{r}{\sqrt[3]{V}}$. (See Table 15, Appendix.)

In carrying out a measurement, one accurately determines the weight of a series of drops (of the liquid under investigation) which have been allowed to form very slowly on a specially prepared tip. From the average weight of one drop, its volume is determined $\left(V = \frac{m}{d}\right)$. The radius of the tip is accurately measured. F is taken from Table 15, and the surface tension found by solving for γ in Equation 2:

$$\gamma = \frac{mg}{2\pi r F} \tag{3}$$

Having once determined surface tension, it is possible to calculate any of the constants outlined in Experiment 5.

Apparatus [2] and Chemicals required:

Thermostat with glass sides, thermometer, student drop-weight apparatus, made by sealing about 20 cm. of capillary tubing (6-mm. diam. and 1.5-mm. bore) to a 10-c.c. pipette, and bending it to the form shown in Fig. 7.

Large weighing bottle (75 × 35 mm.) fitted with a two-hole rubber stopper, 2 glass-stoppered weighing bottles (40 × 25 mm.), glass and rubber tubing, 2 Hoffman clamps, micrometer calipers.

Chromic acid cleaning solution, sodium hydroxide solution, distilled water and benzene for investigation.

The assembled apparatus is shown in Fig. 7, on next page.

It is of the utmost importance that the tip of the dropping pipette be ground to a plane surface, perpendicular to the axis of the tube, and that the edges of this surface be free from chips and flaws. This is most conveniently done by carefully clamping the lower portion of the pipette in a block of brass, as in Fig. 8, filling the space between the glass and the countersunk portion of the block with deKotinsky cement, or Wood's metal. The

[2] The complete apparatus may be obtained from the W. M. Welch Manufacturing Co., Chicago.

tip is then ground by hand with 180-mesh silicon carbide and 3F emery on a glass plate, until observation shows it to be perfect. The brass block is then removed, and the tip thoroughly cleaned.

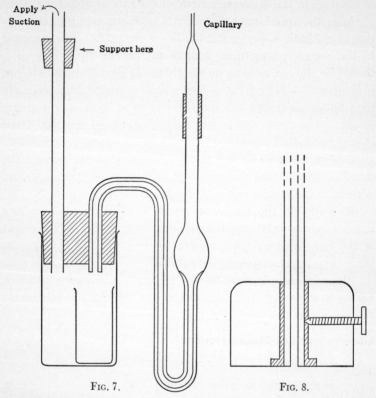

FIG. 7.   FIG. 8.

Method of Procedure:

The glass parts of the apparatus should be carefully cleaned with hot chromic acid, and the rubber parts boiled with sodium hydroxide solution to remove all traces of grease.

Place in the dropping pipette a quantity of the liquid to be investigated sufficient to bring the level in the bulb slightly higher than the level in the tip, and clamp the apparatus vertically in the thermostat, with a clean, dry, and weighed weighing bottle in place beneath the tip.

The upper arm of the pipette should be connected to a glass tube drawn out to a fine capillary, as shown, and the glass tube entering the receiving vessel should have a length of rubber tubing connected to it. These accessories are for the purpose of assisting in the accurate control of the rate of drop formation.

After the apparatus and contents have attained the temperature of the bath, apply gentle suction to the rubber tube attached to the receiver, and draw a drop out on the tip. This drop should be allowed to hang on the tip for at least 5 minutes before it is allowed to fall off by its own weight. Succeeding drops are then drawn to almost full size, then allowed to grow to full size slowly. The total time for formation of succeeding drops should be about 1 minute.

Collect 20 drops in the manner outlined above, remove the weighing bottle from the receiving tube, stopper it quickly, and determine the weight of the 20 drops.

Re-assemble the apparatus, draw 5 more drops in a new tared weighing bottle, and determine their weight. The weight of the last 5 drops drawn, subtracted from that of the first 20, gives the corrected weight of 15 drops.

Measure the diameter of the tip with micrometer calipers, taking it across at least 4 diameters. (Use care not to damage the tip during this operation.)

Observations and Measurements:

Liquid used ......   Temperature ....

Weight, first weighing bottle + (20) drops   ......g.
Weight, first weighing bottle   ......
    Weight (20) drops   ......

Weight, second weighing bottle + (5) drops   ......
Weight, second weighing bottle   ......
    Weight (5) drops   ......

Corrected weight (15) drops   ......
    Weight per drop   ......

Diameter of tip ......cm.
    Mean ......cm.   Radius......

Calculated $\dfrac{r}{\sqrt[3]{V}} = \ldots\ldots$ $F = \ldots\ldots$

Surface tension (calculated) $\ldots\ldots$
Value given in literature $\ldots\ldots$

Calculations:

1. Calculate the surface tension, and compare it with the value given in the literature.

2. Calculate the value of the constant k in the Ramsay and Shields equation, having ascertained from tables the critical temperature of the liquid investigated.

3. If the liquid is associated, calculate the degree of association.

EXPERIMENT 7

VISCOSITY

Object:

To measure relative viscosity and determine the viscosity-composition curve for a two-component liquid system.

Discussion:

The absolute viscosity of a liquid is defined as the force required to move a plane of unit area at unit velocity with respect to another parallel plane separated by unit distance, the space between the planes being filled with the liquid under observation. Absolute viscosity (η) may be measured by observing the rate of flow through capillary tubes, and applying Poiseuille's Law:

$$\eta = \frac{dp \cdot g\pi r^4}{8\,vl}$$

where: dp is the pressure drop across the tube in gm./cm.^{2},

g the acceleration due to gravity in cm./sec.^{2},

r the radius of the tube in cm.,

v the volume delivered in unit time in c.c./sec.,

and l the length of the tube in cm.

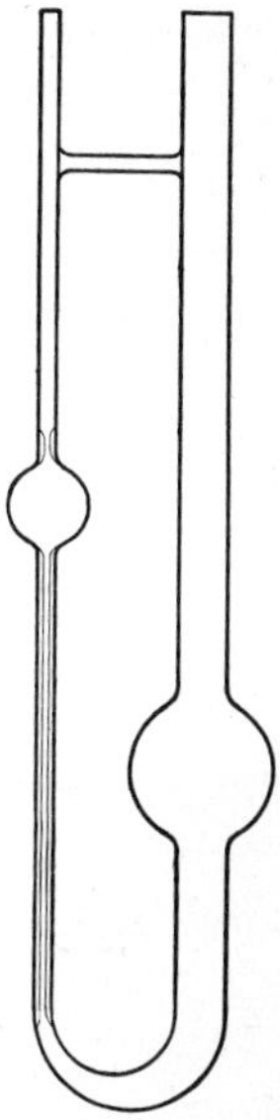

The direct measurement of absolute viscosity is a somewhat difficult procedure.

The relative viscosity of a liquid is the ratio of its absolute viscosity to that of water at the same temperature. Relative viscosities may easily be measured by means of the Ostwald viscosimeter, Fig. 9. Using this instrument,

Fig. 9.

29

the following relationship exists between the absolute viscosities
of two fluids:

$$\eta_1 : \eta_2 = d_1 t_1 : d_2 t_2$$

where: d represents density,
and t outflow time.

Apparatus and Chemicals Required:

Large beaker for constant temperature bath, Ostwald viscosimeter,
stop-watch, binary liquid system made up to contain 0, 20, 40, 60, 80 and
100 molar per cent of liquid B, Westphal balance.

Method of Procedure:

A. *Standardization of the Viscosimeter.*

Thoroughly clean the instrument with hot chromic acid
cleaning solution, then rinse with distilled water, and dry.
Pipette the proper amount of distilled water into the instrument,
clamp it vertically in the constant temperature bath, and allow
the temperature to reach 20° C.   Be certain that the feed bulb
of the instrument is immersed in the bath.

Attach a short length of rubber tubing to the small arm of the
viscosimeter, and draw the liquid over into the feed bulb.   Allow
it to run back of its own accord, recording the time required for
the upper meniscus to successively pass the two calibration
marks.

Repeat until check determinations are obtained.

B. *Determinations of relative Viscosities.*

Prepare solutions of an assigned pair of consolute liquids
with 0, 20, 40, 60, 80 and 100 molar per cent B.   Determine
the outflow time for each of these solutions, as directed
under A.

Determine the density of each solution at 20° C., using either
a Westphal balance or a pyknometer.

Observations and Measurements:

Liquid system assigned: ......
Temperature of the system: 7....
Outflow time for water: .. 121 .. .. Density .. 1
Outflow time for liquid A: .. 84.. .. Density .981
Outflow time for 20 molar per cent B: .. .. Density ....
Outflow time for 40 molar per cent B: .. .. Density ....
Outflow time for 60 molar per cent B: .. .. Density ....
Outflow time for 80 molar per cent B: .. .. Density ....
Outflow time for liquid B: .. .. Density ....

	A	20 molar per cent B	40 molar per cent B
Relative viscosity:	......	......	......
Absolute viscosity	......	......	......

	60 molar per cent B	80 molar per cent B	B
Relative viscosity	......	......	......
Absolute viscosity	......	......	......

Calculations:

1. Calculate the relative viscosity of each liquid and solution.
2. Calculate the absolute viscosity of each liquid and solution. (Consult Table 16, of the Appendix.)
3. Plot the viscosity-composition diagram for the system $A–B$.

Weight of H_2O ---- — — — -- 64.362 g.
Weight of C_6H_6 - — — — — ---- 63.165 g.
Density of C_6H_6 --- - — ---- .981
Time for H_2O flow   121 sec.
   "   " C_6H_6 "   84 "

$\eta_1 : \eta_2 :: d_1 t_1 : d_2 t_2$

η_2 -- - .   .00713

over.

$.01004 : n_2 = 1 \times 1213 \cdot 981 \times 84$

$$n_2 = .00713$$

$$\frac{3.165}{4.362} = \Delta g \, Q_i \, N_2$$

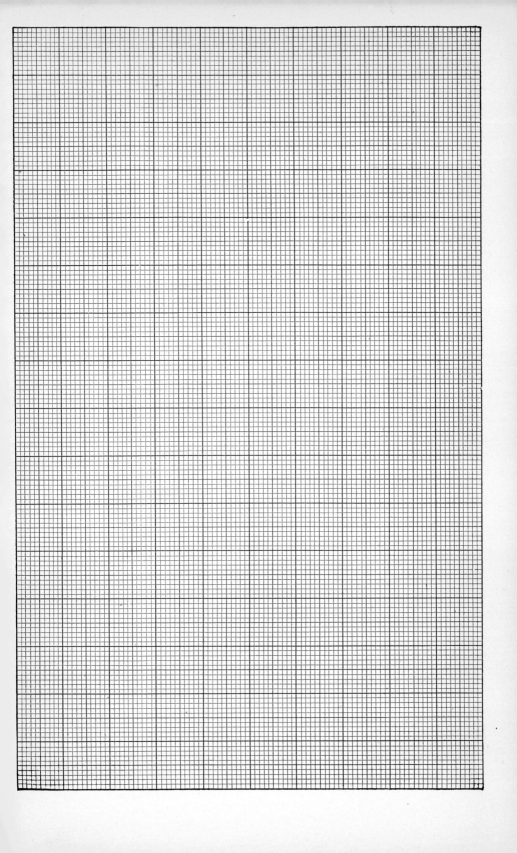

REFRACTIVE INDEX, DENSITY AND MOLECULAR REFRACTIVITY OF LIQUIDS

Object:

To determine the index of refraction and the density of a given liquid and to find its specific and molecular refractivity.

Discussion:

When a monochromatic ray of light passes from one transparent, isotropic medium into another, it is refracted, and the degree of refraction is such that the ratio, n, of the sines of the angles of incidence and refraction is constant and equal to the ratio of the velocities of the light in the two media. This is the well-known law of Snell:

$$n = \frac{\sin i}{\sin r} = \frac{v_1}{v_2}$$

In order to make n a definite, characteristic constant for a given substance, v_1 is referred to the velocity of light in vacuo. Since this velocity is a maximum value, n is always > unity. For light of different wave length, v_1 is only the same in an evacuated space; in any other medium the light velocity and hence n varies with the wave length.

Ordinarily air is chosen as the reference medium. In that case the refractive index with respect to air must be multiplied by the ratio $v_{vacuum}/v_{air} = 1.00029$, in order to get the true refractive index. Except for work of the highest accuracy this correction is often not applied.

In the types of refractometers commonly employed for the determination of n, the light is made to pass at an angle of incidence = 90° from the medium for which n is to be found into a glass cell of known high refractive index (N). The angle at which the ray emerges into air (i) is measured and enables one to calculate n:

$$n = \sqrt{N^2 - \sin^2 i} \qquad (1)$$

The index of refraction depends on the wave length used, as stated before, but also on the conditions which affect the density of the medium, such as temperature and pressure. In order to express the " refractive power " of a medium in such a way that it is independent of variations in temperature and pressure the terms specific refraction, r, and molecular refraction are calculated from n and d (density).

According to Gladstone and Dale

$$r = \frac{n - 1}{d} \qquad (2)$$

Lorenz–Lorentz proposed the formula:

$$r = \frac{1}{d} \cdot \frac{n^2 - 1}{n^2 + 2} \qquad (3)$$

The molecular refraction is obtained by multiplying the specific refraction by the molecular weight of the substance.

Apparatus and Chemicals required:

Refractometer, thermostat, preferably at 20° C. Pyknometer.
Bottle containing distilled water, sample bottles containing different organic liquids, silk paper, to clean prisms of refractometer.

Fig. 10 represents the Abbe refractometer, which is widely used in this country and is most satisfactory for general laboratory practice, as it is easy to handle and is so constructed that it can be used with daylight and gives values corresponding to the " D " line. For accurate setting it is necessary, however, to use sodium light (see p. 129). It consists of two prisms of flint glass with a refractive index of 1.75 which can be separated so as to allow the introduction of a few drops of liquid. The prisms can be rotated by means of a movable arm M which carries the reading glass R. The position of the border line of total reflection is observed through the fixed telescope T, and by turning the movable arm it is made to coincide with the intersection of the cross hairs in the telescope. The arc A is graduated so as to read directly refractive indices (between 1.3 and 1.7) to the third decimal place. The fourth decimal is estimated with an accuracy of 2 units by means of the lens

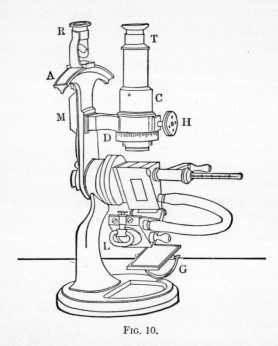

Fig. 10.

R. The compensator C composed of two similar Amici prisms, rotated simultaneously in opposite directions by the milled head H, is used to produce a dispersion $(C—F)$ equal but opposite to that of the liquid and permits the border line to be changed from a colored band to a sharp colorless line. By taking the reading on the divided drum D and using the table supplied with the instrument the dispersion may also be found. A heating arrangement furnished by the makers, or else a large thermostat permits the circulation of water at a given temperature through the casing of the prisms.

Method of Procedure:

Place the instrument on a table near the window, but not in direct sunlight, and provide a large constant temperature bath, making connections for the circulation of the water through the casings in a slow but steady stream.

Turn the latch L, release the lower prism and swing it into the position shown in Fig. 10.

In order to test the correctness of the adjustment of the refractometer, place a drop of distilled water on the glass surface, close the prisms and secure them by means of the latch L, rotate the prisms by turning the movable arm (also rotate the mirror G in such a way that it reflects light on the prisms) until the border line appears in the field.

Turn the screw head H and thereby adjust the compensator so that the colored band due to dispersion disappears and a sharp boundary line is obtained.

Finally rotate the arm M until the line coincides with the intersection of the cross hairs and take the reading to the fourth decimal place. Also read the temperature.

Repeat the readings at least three times and take the mean, comparing the result with the data given for water on Table 3 of the Appendix.

Open the latch, drop the lower prism, clean the polished glass surfaces with a little alcohol and silk paper (do not use filter paper) and operate on the liquid(s) assigned for investigation in exactly the same manner as outlined above.

In order to be able to calculate the molecular refractivity it is necessary to determine the density of the liquid at the temperature for which the readings were taken. Any of the well-known types of pyknometers may be used.

The density is given by the formula:

$$d_{4^{\circ}}^{t^{\circ}} = \frac{W'D}{W} - \frac{0.0012\,(W' - W)}{W}$$

where: W' is the weight of liquid at $t°$,
    W the weight of water at $t°$,
and D the density of water at $t°$ (see Table 4 of the Appendix).

The small fraction to be subtracted is a correction for the buoyancy of the air.

Find the weight of the pyknometer, first empty and then filled with water of the same temperature.

Observations and Measurements:

  A. *Refractometer Measurements:*

    Water at ....° C.   Refractive index: ......
                   ......
                   ......
                   ......

             Average value:
              Value given:
    Liquid used: ....
    Temperature ....° C. Refractive index: ......
                   ......
                   ......
                   ......

             Average value:
  B. *Pyknometer Measurements:*

    Weight pyknometer empty: .... g.
    Same filled with water at ....° C.   .... g.
    Same filled with liquid at ....° C.   .... g.

Calculations:

  1. From the observations under A and B calculate the specific and the molecular refractivity of the liquid under observation, using both the Gladstone–Dale and the Lorenz–Lorentz formulæ, and compare the values obtained with those given in the literature (see the tables of Landolt–Börnstein).

EXPERIMENT 9

SOLUBILITY. THE VAN'T HOFF ISOCHORE

Object:

To determine the solubility of a solid at two different temperatures, and to calculate its heat of solution at the mean temperature by means of the van't Hoff isochore.

Discussion:

The solubility of a solid is conveniently determined by agitating an excess of the solute with the solvent until equilibrium is established, filtering a portion of the saturated solution, and analyzing it for amount of solute and solvent present.

The van't Hoff isochore, as applied to solubility work, may be written as follows:

$$\frac{d(\log_e K_c)}{dT} = \frac{Q}{RT^2}$$

where Q is the heat of solution and K_c the solubility.

Differentiating this equation between narrow temperature limits in which the heat of solution does not change materially, making R equal to 1.99 calories, and passing to Briggsian logarithms, we obtain:

$$\log K_{c_2} - \log K_{c_1} = \frac{Q}{4.581} \times \frac{(T_2 - T_1)}{T_1 T_2}$$

In the above equation, K_{c_1} and K_{c_2} are the solubilities at the two absolute temperatures T_1 and T_2, respectively, and Q is the heat of solution, in calories per mole.

Apparatus and Chemicals required:

Two thermostats fitted for solubility work, one to be held at 25°, the other at 45° C., four 4-oz. oil-sample bottles, one 50-c.c. and one 10-c.c. pipette, short rubber tubes and cotton for filters, burette and holder, 125-c.c. Erlenmeyer flask.

N/4 alkali, distilled water, powdered benzoic acid, phenolphthalein indicator solution.

Method of Procedure:

Place from two to three grams of powdered benzoic acid in each of two 4-oz. oil-sample bottles, add about 75 c.c. of water, cork the bottles tightly, label them No. 1 and No. 2, and attach them to the rotating device in the 25° thermostat.

Place between 5 and 6 grams of benzoic acid in each of two bottles No. 3 and No. 4, cork them, and attach them to the rotator in the 45° thermostat.

The samples should be agitated in the thermostats at least 2 hours, before proceeding with the experiment. When it is possible to do so, start the experiment one day and allow it to run until the next before making the analyses.

Prepare half a dozen small filters for the pipettes by *loosely* filling small lengths of rubber tubing with cotton. Disconnect bottle No. 1, place it in a vertical position in such a way that its neck is just above the water in the thermostat, and remove the cork. Attach one of the filters to the pipette, and suck up a little over 50 c.c. of the solution. Remove the filter, and adjust the contents of the pipette to the mark.

Transfer the sample to an Erlenmeyer flask, boil carefully, and titrate with N/4 alkali, using phenolphthalein as indicator.

Analyze the solutions in bottles 2, 3 and 4 in like manner, withdrawing 10-c.c. samples from bottles 3 and 4, and diluting them with 40 c.c. of distilled water before titration.

Assuming that the density of each solution is unity, calculate the weight of benzoic acid present in each sample per 100 gms. of water.

Observations and Measurements:

Temperature of first thermostat: . . . .
Temperature of second thermostat: . . . .

	Sample No. 1 c.c.	Sample No. 2 c.c.
Amount of alkali used for titration:	. . . . . .	. . . . . .
Normality of benzoic acid:	. . . . . .	. . . . . .
Benzoic acid per 100 gms. of H_2O:	. . . . . . g.	. . . . . . g.

Average: . . . . . . g.

	Sample No. 3 c.c.	Sample No. 4 c.c.
Amount of alkali used for titration:	. . . . . .	. . . . . .
Normality of benzoic acid:	. . . . . .	. . . . . .
Benzoic acid per 100 gms. of H_2O:	. . . . . . g.	. . . . . . g.

. . . . g.

Average:

Calculations:

1. Calculate the solubility of benzoic acid per 100 gms. of water for each sample.

2. Calculate the heat of solution, using the mean values obtained under 1.

EXPERIMENT 10

LOWERING OF THE FREEZING POINT.
BECKMANN METHOD

Object:

(a) To determine the molecular weight of a non-electrolyte.

(b) To determine the apparent molecular weight of an electrolyte and to calculate its degree of dissociation at the concentrations employed.

Discussion:

In the Beckmann method for determining approximate or apparent molecular weights by lowering of the freezing point, the freezing point of the pure solvent is carefully determined by means of a Beckmann differential thermometer; then a small weighed quantity of the solute whose approximate molecular weight is to be determined, is dissolved in a known quantity of solvent (giving a dilute solution) and the freezing point of this solution is accurately determined. The equation for calculating approximate molecular weights from these data is as follows:

$$M = \frac{100 K_f g}{G dT}$$

where: M is the molecular weight,

K_f the freezing point constant for the solvent employed (18.6 for water),

g the weight of the solute,

dT the freezing point lowering,

and G the weight of solvent present.

If the solute dissociates in the solvent used, the above formula gives the so-called " apparent " molecular weight. If n, the number of ions into which one molecule of the solute dissociates, is known, the degree of dissociation (α) may be estimated from the apparent molecular weight in the following manner:

Let i represent the true molecular weight divided by the apparent molecular weight. Then

$$\alpha = \frac{i - 1}{n - 1}$$

Apparatus and Chemicals required:

Beckmann freezing-point apparatus, differential thermometer, 2 stirrers, reading glass, 10-c.c. pipette, ice and salt for producing a freezing mixture, sample bottles with various electrolytes and non-electrolytes.

The apparatus is shown in Fig. 11. A mixture of water, crushed ice and salt, sufficient to reach within an inch of the top, is placed in the large glass jar. The air jacket is fixed in this freezing mixture through the central aperture of the cover, and serves to prevent direct contact between the Beckmann freezing-point tube and the cooling bath.

Method of Procedure:

Prepare a freezing mixture and maintain its temperature around $-5°$.

By means of a 10-c.c. pipette introduce sufficient distilled water into the freezing tube to immerse the bulb of the Beckmann thermometer. Make each addition exactly 10 c.c. The mass of water used is determined by noting the temperature and obtaining the weight from Table 4, Appendix. Place the thermometer and stirrer in position in such a manner that the stirrer moves freely, and immerse the tube directly in the freezing mixture. It will be noticed that the water supercools several degrees before freezing begins, and that as soon as ice forms the temperature rises rapidly, approaching the freezing point (heat being liberated by the separation of ice).

Take the freezing-point tube from the cold bath, wipe it dry and place it in the air bath, allowing equilibrium to be attained. Stir gently, tapping the stem of the thermometer at regular intervals and record readings every 30 seconds, estimating thousandths of a degree by means of a reading glass. The value obtained when readings have become constant is taken as the freezing point of pure water. Plot these results on coordinate paper. Melt the ice and repeat the determination. Successive observations should agree to within 0.002° before proceeding.

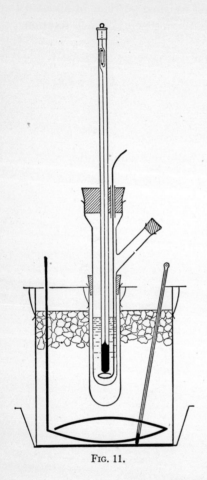

FIG. 11.

Introduce about half a gram of solute, accurately weighed, and determine the freezing point of the solution. Inasmuch as the separation of the solid phase (ice) concentrates the solution, it is necessary to exercise extreme care in having the smallest possible amount of ice present at the time of final temperature reading. In case this precaution is not observed, results will be vitiated. When operating on solutions, it is best not to immerse the freezing-point tube directly in the cold freezing mixture. Should it, however, be necessary to do this in order to initiate the crystallization, it is advisable to melt the greater portion of the ice by holding the tube in the hand before placing it in the air bath. As before, record readings every 30 seconds until the equilibrium temperature has been located, and plot these values, taking the maximum temperature on the temperature-time curve.

Add two successive additional weighed portions of about 0.2 gm. of solute, and determine the freezing point of each solution.

Observations and Measurements:

Volume of distilled water used.......... *40* — c.c.

Temperature *20* . °

Density (from Table 4) *.9982*

Weight of water used.. *37.928* .... — g.

Thermometer readings at half-minute intervals:

Water	Solution 1	Solution 2	Solution 3
4.78	......	*4.11*	......
4.64	*4.21*	*4.17*	......
4.48	*4.20*	*4.145*	......
4.34	*4.20*	*4.147*	......
4.28	*4.195*	*4.145*	......
4.12	*4.193*	*4.145*	......
4.06	*4.190*	*4.145*	......
3.91	*4.192*	*4.145*	......
3.80	*4.191*	*4.145*	......
3.76	*4.191*	*4.145*	......
4.24	......	......	......
4.245	......	......	......
4.245	......	......	......
4.245	......	......	......
4.245	......	......	......
4.245	......	......	......
......	......	......	......
......	......	......	......
......	......	......	......
......	......	......	......

Solute added. *Suchrose*

Weight in g.   *.5gm*   *.2gm*   ......

Lowering of freez-
ing point   *.055* °   *.1* °   ......°

Calculations:

    A. Solute is a non-electrolyte:
        1. Calculate the molecular weight of the solute for each
           concentration used. Obtain freezing-point constant
           from Table 5, Appendix.

    B. Solute is an electrolyte:
        1. Calculate the apparent molecular weight of the solute
           for each concentration used.
        2. Compute the degree of dissociation for each apparent
           molecular weight.
        3. Plot apparent molecular weight, and degree of dis-
           sociation, against concentration, expressed in grams
           of solute per 100 grams of solvent.

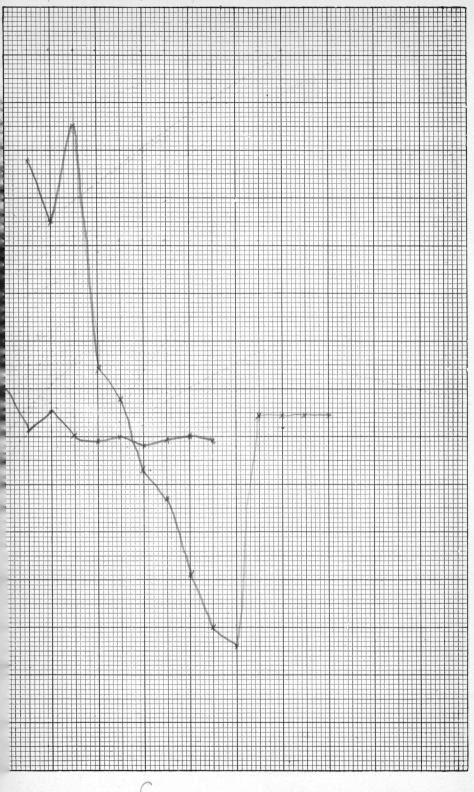

1   2   3   4

C

EXPERIMENT 11

LOWERING OF THE FREEZING POINT.
DEWAR VACUUM-FLASK METHOD

Object:

To determine the approximate molecular weight of a non-electrolyte, or the apparent molecular weight and degree of dissociation of an electrolyte, by the lowering of the freezing point, using the vacuum-flask method.[1]

Discussion:

The standard Beckmann method for molecular-weight determination by observations on the lowering of the freezing point possesses an inherent source of error. One determines the concentration of the solution being investigated by weighing both solvent and solute. When freezing takes place in dilute aqueous solutions ice separates and the solution becomes more concentrated. One is, therefore unable to estimate the *exact* composition of the liquid phase at the freezing point. Obviously some method of *analyzing the solution* at the time when temperature readings are recorded will overcome this error.

In the vacuum-flask method, concentrations are determined by chemical analyses. Finely shaved ice, and an aqueous solution of the solute under observation, are thoroughly stirred in a vacuum flask until equilibrium is reached between the two phases. The temperature is noted, and samples of the solution are withdrawn for analysis by suitable methods.

The usual freezing-point equation, given on page 44, applies to the calculations.

[1] Roloff, Zeits. f. phys. Chemie, **18**, 572 (1895); Ponsot, Ann. chim. phys. (7), **10**, 79 (1897); Richards, J.A.C.S., **25**, 29 (1903).

Apparatus and Chemicals Required:

One wide-mouth vacuum flask (one-quart fruit jar) fitted with a protecting jacket, stirrer, and cork stopper carrying (a) the Beckmann thermometer, (b) a long glass tube terminating near the bulb of the thermometer for withdrawing samples, (c) a short tube for the introduction of samples, and (d) a hole for the stirrer, ice shaver, one 2-c.c., one 5-c.c., and one 10-c.c. pipette, three 125-c.c. and six 50-c.c. Erlenmeyer flasks.

A. The solute is an electrolyte (acid or base).

N/10 alkali or acid, phenolphthalein, burette and holder, approximately 10 per cent acid or base.

B. The solute is a non-electrolyte (urea).

Two 2-compartment gas evolution bottles, with means for connecting them to a 100-c.c. graduated gas-measuring tube, 1 leveling tube, one 0°–110° thermometer, small bottle containing freshly made saturated urea solution, bottle containing fresh sodium hypobromite solution (prepared by dissolving 100 gms. of NaOH in 250 c.c. of water, and slowly adding 25 c.c. of bromine).

The assembled freezing-point apparatus is shown in Fig. 12. The gas-evolution apparatus for analyzing urea solutions is illustrated in Fig. 13.

Method of Procedure:

Determination of the lowering of the freezing point:

Fill the vacuum flask with shaved ice. It is important that the ice be shaved, and not merely cracked. Add sufficient cold distilled water to permit the stirrer to move freely.

" Set " the Beckmann thermometer, assemble the apparatus, stir regularly, and take temperature readings at half-minute intervals until constant values have been obtained. This constant value is taken as the freezing point of pure water.

By means of a small pipette, introduce sufficient solution of the solute to be investigated to lower the freezing point of the contents of the flask about one-quarter of one degree, and determine the freezing point of the solution by the method outlined above.

Without delay, insert the 10-c.c. pipette through the sample withdrawal tube so that its tip is near the thermometer bulb. Withdraw about 5 c.c. of solution, rinse the pipette with this,

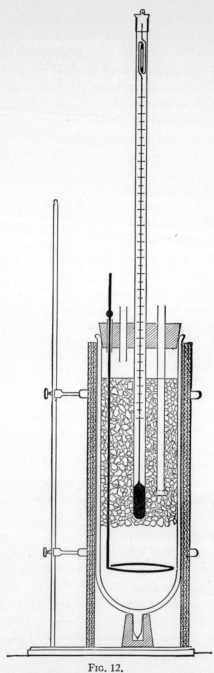

Fig. 12.

then withdraw two 10-c.c. samples for analysis. These samples must be taken from the region around the thermometer bulb. In case the analysis does not give results that check, additional samples must be taken until concordant values are obtained.

When two checks have been obtained, add two additional quantities of the solute (to obtain total lowerings of about one-half and three-quarters of a degree, respectively), determine the freezing points, and withdraw samples for analysis as before.

Analysis of the samples:

A. The solute is an acid or base. Titrate the 10-c.c. samples which were withdrawn from the vacuum flask with tenth-normal base or alkali, using phenolphthalein, or some other suitable indicator. Record the results of the analyses in the proper place under " Observations and Measurements."

B. The solute is urea. Carefully place the sample to be evaluated in one compartment of a gas-evolution flask, and in the other compartment place 25 c.c. of the sodium hypobromite solution. Exercise care that the two solutions do not mix.

Bring the water in the gas-measuring tube to the zero point, and connect the gas-evolution flask to this tube, as shown in Fig. 13.

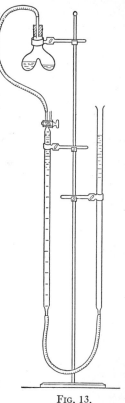

FIG. 13.

As soon as the apparatus has attained uniform temperature, level up the water and take the initial reading. Then so manipulate the gas-evolution bottle that the two solutions it contains are thoroughly mixed. Gentle shaking will assist the evolution of gas. As fast as gas is evolved, lower the leveling tube in order to maintain atmospheric pressure within the system.

When the gas evolution is complete, allow the system to

attain room temperature; then level the water and record the volume, temperature, and pressure.

The other samples are analyzed in similar manner.

Following the procedure outlined above, 1 c.c. of gas (nitrogen) collected, *under standard conditions* is equivalent to 0.00288 gm. of urea.

When two students are working together, it is advisable that one carries out the freezing-point determinations, while the other performs the analyses.

Observations and Measurements:

A. Electrolytes (acids or bases):

Temperature Readings at Half-minute Intervals

Ice Water	Solution 1	Solution 2	Solution 3
. . . . . .	. . . . . .	. . . . . .	. . . . . .
. . . . . .	. . . . . .	. . . . . .	. . . . . .
. . . . . .	. . . . . .	. . . . . .	. . . . . .
. . . . . .	. . . . . .	. . . . . .	. . . . . .
. . . . . .	. . . . . .	. . . . . .	. . . . . .
. . . . . .	. . . . . .	. . . . . .	. . . . . .
. . . . . .	. . . . . .	. . . . . .	. . . . . .
. . . . . .	. . . . . .	. . . . . .	. . . . . .
. . . . . .	. . . . . .	. . . . . .	. . . . . .
. . . . . .	. . . . . .	. . . . . .	. . . . . .
. . . . . .	. . . . . .	. . . . . .	. . . . . .
. . . . . .	. . . . . .	. . . . . .	. . . . . .

Analysis of the samples.

Normality of base (or acid) . . . .

Volume of base (or acid) used in the titrations:

Sample 1   . . . .
Sample 2   . . . .
Average   . . . .

Normality   . . . .

Gms. solute/100 gms. of H_2O ....
Apparent mol. wt.   ....
Degree of dissociation   ....

B. Urea:

Temperature Readings

Ice Water	Solution 1	Solution 2	Solution 3
......	......	......	......
......	......	......	......
......	......	......	......
......	......	......	......
......	......	......	......
......	......	......	......
......	......	......	......
......	......	......	......
......	......	......	......
......	......	......	......
......	......	......	......
......	......	......	......

Nitrometer readings before and after gas evolution:

Sample 1.   ....
Sample 2.   ....
Average   ....

Barometer reading...mm. Corrected...mm. Room Temp...°
Vapor pressure of water...mm. Corrected gas pressure...mm.
Volume of gas collected (S.C)   ....
Gms. urea/100 gms. of H_2O ....
Molecular weight of urea   ....

Calculations:

1. Calculate the molecular weight (or the apparent molecular weight).

2. Plot molecular weight against concentration.

3. If the solute is an electrolyte, calculate the degree of dissociation for each dilution, and plot degree of dissociation against concentration.

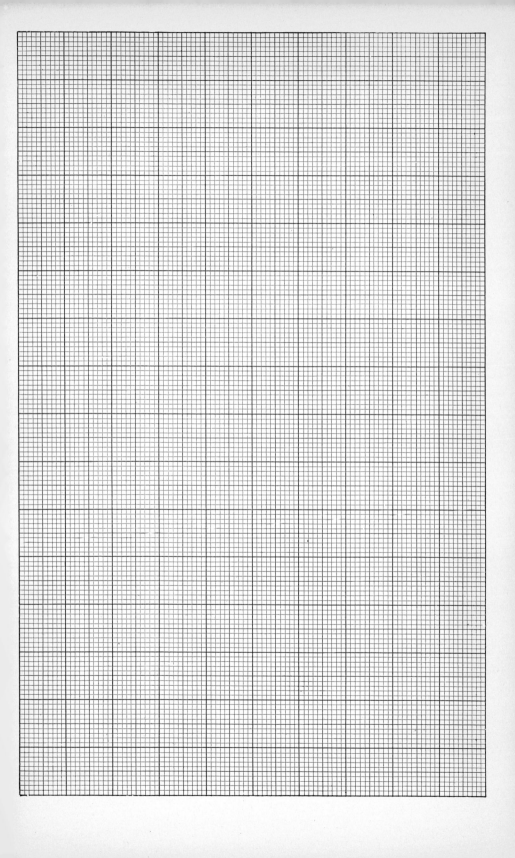

EXPERIMENT 12

ELEVATION OF THE BOILING POINT.
THE COTTRELL APPARATUS

Object:

To determine molecular weights of substances in solution by the elevation of boiling-point method.

Discussion:

We have already seen (Experiments 11 and 10) how the approximate molecular weight of a substance in solution may be deter-

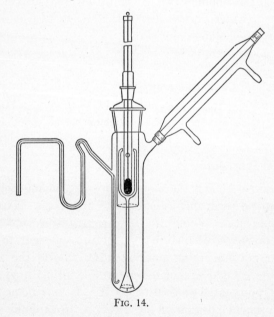

FIG. 14.

mined by observations on the lowering of the freezing point. The same type of information is obtained from observations on the elevation of the boiling point, but the results are somewhat less accurate on account of the fact that the constants are smaller, and that slight variations in pressure and rate of boiling affect the thermometer readings.

The Cottrell boiling-point apparatus,[1] Fig. 14, is probably the most satisfactory device for boiling-point work. It embodies a jet device which keeps the thermometer bulb bathed in a stream of boiling liquid which has had opportunity to lose its superheat, and thus eliminates variations due to differing rates of boiling.

The equation used is similar to that given in the freezing-point method:

$$M = \frac{100 K_b g}{G dT}$$

where: M is the approximate (or apparent) molecular weight of the solute,

K_b the boiling-point constant for the solvent (5.2 for water),

dT the boiling-point rise,

and g and G the weight of solute and solvent, respectively.

Apparatus and Chemicals required:

Cottrell boiling-point apparatus, fitted with Beckmann thermometer and reflux condenser, micro-burner, weighing bottles containing solutes for observation.

Method of Procedure:

Set the Beckmann thermometer for the boiling point of the solvent to be used and assemble the apparatus. Place a few bits of pumice or porous tile in the apparatus, and run in a weighed or measured quantity of solvent sufficient to immerse the lower portion of the guard mantle. Shield the apparatus from drafts. Light the micro-burner, and adjust it so that boiling and " pumping " proceed regularly. It may be necessary to alter the size or position of the flame, or to carefully raise and lower the inner assembly, or to add more solvent, in order to

[1] Cottrell, J.A.C.S., **41**, 721 (1919); Washburn, *ibid.*, **41**, 729 (1919).

start pumping. Once this action has been established at a regular rate, do not alter the flame.

Determine the boiling point of the pure solvent by taking half-minute readings until constant results are obtained. Gently tap the thermometer before each reading is made.

Weigh and introduce sufficient solute into the apparatus to obtain a rise in boiling point of about one-tenth of a degree. Determine the boiling point of this solution.

Make two more weighed additions of solute, determining the boiling point each time.

(*Note:* For work of the highest accuracy, samples of solution may be withdrawn and analyzed after each boiling-point determination.)

Observations and Measurements:

Solvent	Solute ......
Barometric reading at start	Corr. ......
Barometric reading at end	Corr. ......
Grams of solvent used	

Temperature Readings:

Pure solvent	Sol. No. 1	Sol. No. 2	Sol. No 3
......	......	......	......
......	......	......	......
......	......	......	......
......	......	......	......
......	......	......	......
......	......	......	......
......	......	......	......
......	......	......	......
......	......	......	......
......	......	......	......
Gms. of solute added		......	......
	......	......	......
	......	......	......

Calculations:

1. Calculate the approximate (or apparent) molecular weight for each dilution.

2. If the solute is an electrolyte, calculate the degree of dissociation.

3. Plot molecular weights and degrees of dissociation against concentration.

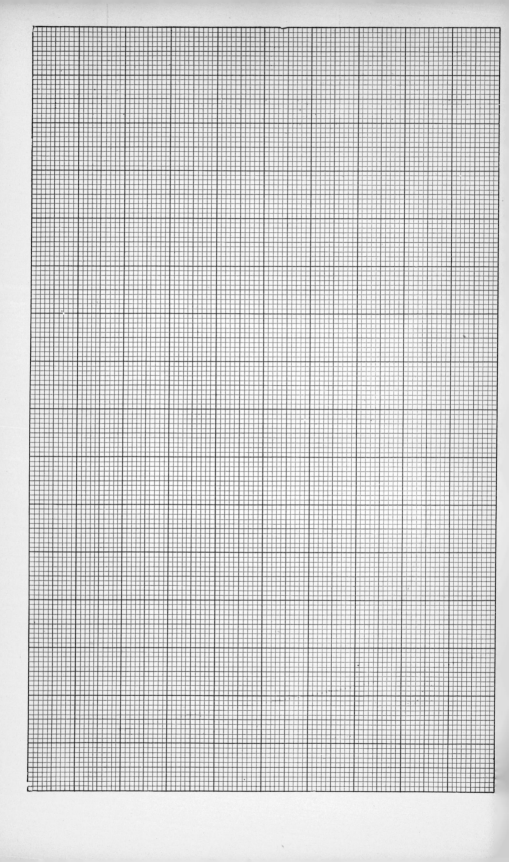

EXPERIMENT 13

ELEVATION OF THE BOILING POINT.
THE EYKMAN METHOD

Object:

To determine approximate molecular weights, using Eykman's apparatus.

Discussion:

The boiling-point molecular-weight apparatus devised by Eykman [1] gives entirely satisfactory results when used with low-boiling solvents such as CCl_4. It possesses the advantages of neither requiring a Beckmann thermometer, nor a separate condenser; and the quantity of solvent may be estimated directly from the position of the upper meniscus on the thermometer scale.

The usual boiling-point formula (see page 59) is used for the calculations.

Apparatus and Chemicals required:

Two iron clamps, iron stands, large flanged " Pyrex " tube (50 × 400 mm.), Eykman boiling-point vessel fitting into jacket, thermometer (40–100° C.) graduated in tenths of degrees, micro-burner + rubber tubing, burette + holder, bottle containing pure carbon tetrachloride, bottle for carbon tetrachloride residues, small sample tube with azobenzene.[2]

Fig. 15 gives a sketch of the apparatus. The outer glass jacket A held vertically by means of an iron ring or a clamp serves the double purpose of boiling vessel and air cooler.

The inner boiling-point vessel B (Eykman boiling-point tube), which fits snugly into this mantel, consists of an outer

---

[1] Jour. Chem. Phys., **2**, 47 (1903); Menzies and Wright, J.A.C.S., **43**, 2314 (1921).

[2] CCl_4 is selected for its non-inflammability, and azobenzene for its color, which shows possible residues from a previous experiment at once.

cylinder surrounding and fused at the top to a test tube C. A small bore glass tube D is fused into the bottom of the test tube and passes upward between the walls of the latter and the cylinder. Vapor of the solvent enters the test tube through this small bore tube and brings the solution to boiling.

The Eykman vessel is suspended from a clamp which also holds the thermometer in a central vertical position.

The thermometer should be graduated in tenths of degrees so that hundredths can be estimated by means of a reading glass.

Method of Procedure:

Since both the boiling point and the volume of the solution are read on the thermometer, it is necessary first to calibrate the inner tube volumetrically.

In doing this, raise the inner vessel until its top comes flush

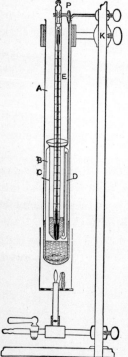

with the top of the outer jacket and make sure that the inner vessel and the thermometer are both exactly vertical. The latter should always rest on the bottom of the inner tube.

From a burette filled to the zero mark with pure carbon tetrachloride, run a whole number of c.c. into the inner tube until the liquid rises to a point where the level can be read on the scale, and record this reading.

Add exactly 1 c.c. at a time, reading the volume each time on the thermometer, until 25 c.c. have been added.

Prepare a table which will show the volume of the solution in the tube at any height shown on the thermometer.

Remove enough of the solvent from the inner tube to bring the level to the bottom of the scale and place about 50 c.c. of pure carbon tetrachloride in the outer jacket.

FIG. 15.

Lower the Eykman vessel so that the bottom of the inner tube is just about 1 cm. above the level of the liquid inside the surrounding cylindrical tube.

Place a small flame under the outer jacket and adjust the flame in such a manner that the vapor condenses about 5 cm. above the top of the Eykman tube (at E, Fig. 15).

Take temperature readings every 15 seconds and record the same. When the thermometer gives a value constant to hundredths of a degree, equilibrium has been reached.

Raise the inner vessel till its top comes flush with the top of the jacket and add from 0.15 to 0.200 gram of azobenzene, accurately weighed, observing care lest some of it stick to the thermometer or the side of the tube.

Lower the vessel to the same level as before, and determine the boiling point of the solution. Be sure that the solution actually boils; this can readily be seen by observing whether the vapor of the solvent bubbles through the solution. If this does not take place the inner vessel should be lowered a little more.

Raise the tube to its previous height, *observe the volume*, using precaution to make sure that conditions are the same as in calibrating. Record volume.

Add successively 3 weighed quantities of azobenzene (0.15–0.200 gram) and note carefully the boiling point and the volume each time, as directed above.

When all the readings have been taken, turn off the gas, remove the thermometer, pour the residue from the vessel into a bottle provided for this purpose and rinse both the thermometer and the tube with a few c.c. of pure carbon tetrachloride, transferring the liquid each time to the residue bottle.

Do not attempt to rinse and clean the apparatus with water.

Observations and Measurements:

Volume readings on thermometer:

....c.c. = ... scale reading .... c.c. = ...

....

....

....

....

....

....

....

....

....

Barometric pressure ....mm. Corrected value ....mm.
Room temperature ....°
Boiling point of pure solvent and of 4 solutions, readings
every 15 seconds:

Added ...gm.	Added ...gm.	Added ...gm.	Added ...gm.
......	......	......	......
......	......	......	......
......	......	......	......
......	......	......	......
......	......	......	......
......	......	......	......
......	......	......	......
......	......	......	......
......	......	......	......
......	......	......	......
......	......	......	......
......	......	......	......
......	......	......	......
......	......	......	......
......	......	......	......
......	......	......	......
......	......	......	......

```
. . . . . .        . . . . . .        . . . . . .        . . . . . .        . . . . . .
. . . . . .        . . . . . .        . . . . . .        . . . . . .        . . . . . .
. . . . . .        . . . . . .        . . . . . .        . . . . . .        . . . . . .
```

Volume readings on thermometer:

```
                   . . . . . .        . . . . . .        . . . . . .        . . . . . .
```
Volume readings in c.c.:

```
                   . . . . . .        . . . . . .        . . . . . .        . . . . . .
```

Calculations:

1. Assuming that the specific gravity of the solutions is practically the same as that of the pure solvent, find the weight of solvent used in each case.

2. Express the four concentrations in terms of grams of solute in 100 grams of solvent [weight of solvent (S): weight of solute (g) = 100 : x]

3. Record the data obtained: Δ (rise of boiling point), S, g, and concentration in following table:

Solution	Δ	S	g	conc.
1	. . . . . .	. . . . . .	. . . . . .	. . . . . .
2	. . . . . .	. . . . . .	. . . , . .	. . . . . .
3	. . . . . .	. . . . . .	. . . . . .	. . . . . .
4	. . . . . .	. . . . . .	. . . . . .	. . . . . .

4. Apply the boiling-point formula and calculate for each concentration the molecular weight of azobenzene. Obtain boiling-point constant from Table 6, Appendix.

5. Plot the molecular weights obtained as a function of the concentrations and connect the points obtained by a straight line. Where it intersects the Y-axis, the value for the molecular weight at infinite dilution which is the nearest approach to the theoretical value, is obtained.

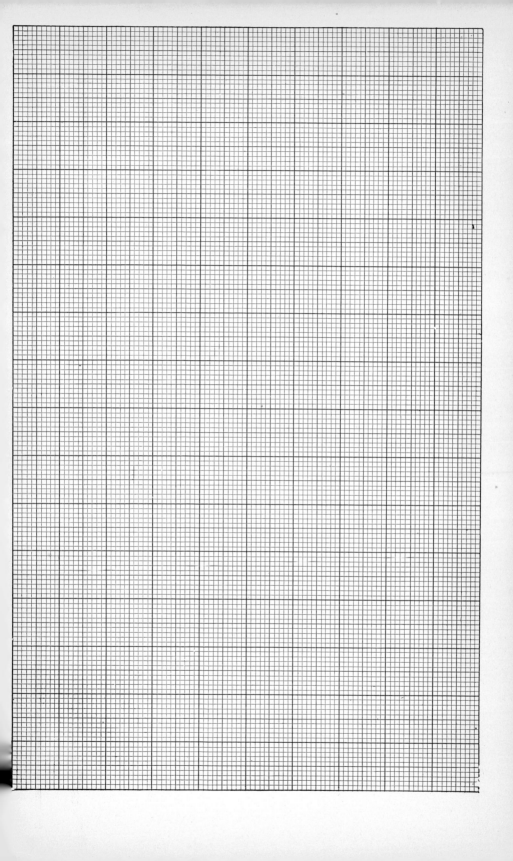

VAPOR PRESSURE LOWERING BY A DISSOLVED SUBSTANCE. RAOULT'S LAW.

Object:

To determine the approximate molecular weight of a sub-- stance in solution from measurements on the lowering of the vapor pressure of the solvent.

Discussion:

Raoult's Law states that when a non-volatile substance is dissolved in a given solvent, the relative lowering of the vapor pressure of the solvent is proportional to the ratio of the number of mols of solute present to the total mols of solute and solvent. It is usually formulated as follows:

$$\frac{p - p'}{p} = \frac{n}{n + N}$$

where: p is the vapor pressure of the solvent,

p' that of the solution,

n the number of mols of solute,

and N the number of mols of solvent.

There are two common methods available for measuring the lowering of vapor pressure, the " air saturation " method, and that of Menzies. In the former, dry air (or other gas) is simul- taneously bubbled through pure solvent and solution held at the same temperature, and the vapor pressure of each determined by analysis of the gas as it leaves the system. This method is probably more exact than the one about to be described, but the time required for its completion is considerably longer.

Menzies' apparatus is shown in Fig. 16. It consists of an outer jacket in which pure solvent is boiled. The vapor of the solvent surrounds an inner chamber, closed at the top by a ground-glass plug; the inner chamber communicates with the outer by means of a small glass tube which serves as a manometer. The lowering of the vapor pressure is read on this manometer arm, which is usually calibrated in millimeters.

FIG. 16.

Apparatus and Chemicals required:

Menzies' apparatus, connected to a short condenser by means of a short length of soft rubber tubing, bottle with solvent (CCl$_4$ recommended), small bottles containing solutes for investigation, iron stand, ring and two large clamps, pinch-cock, micro-burner, and burner shield.

Method of Procedure:

If CCl$_4$ is used as solvent, it is highly important that it be entirely free from traces of water, and that the apparatus and samples of solute be absolutely dry. Do not wash the apparatus with water after finishing the experiment.

The inner vessel is usually calibrated in cubic centimeters. It is advisable to check these calibrations. Ordinarily it will be necessary to calibrate the vessel for volume, noting liquid heights on the millimeter scale of the small manometer tube. This calibration is readily made by running the solvent in from a burette, and noting volumes added, and liquid levels in the vessel.

After the inner tube has been calibrated, half fill the bulb of the outer tube with solvent, assemble the apparatus, and place about 5 c.c. of solvent in the inner vessel. Light the burner and adjust the flame in such a manner that the vapor is completely condensed in the lower 2 inches of the condenser.

It is necessary to expel all the air from the inner tube. This is done by lifting the ground-glass stopper with the right hand, and simultaneously pinching off the rubber tube between the apparatus and the condenser with the left. This causes the vapor to bubble through the inner vessel, and to escape at the top, driving the air ahead of it. This sweeping-out action is stopped by first dropping the plug into its seat, and an instant later releasing the restriction in the rubber tube.

It may be necessary to repeat this sweeping-out procedure several times before the air is all removed from the inner chamber. In general, satisfactory results have been obtained when the liquid rises to the same height in the manometer tube as it would be raised by capillarity. Record this height (above the liquid in the vessel) as the initial height for the apparatus.

With approximately 15 c.c. of solvent in the inner chamber, weigh about 0.2 gram of solute accurately, and carefully dissolve it in this liquid. Sweep the air out several times, and allow the system to come to thermal equilibrium. This is important, because passing vapor of the solvent through the solution causes the latter to boil, and its boiling point is higher than that of the pure solvent. The success of the experiment requires that the difference between the vapor pressure of the solution and that of the solvent be determined at the same temperature, i.e., at the boiling point of the solvent. Hence it is necessary to allow the solution to cool to the temperature of the boiling solvent after each " sweeping-out " procedure.

Record the volume of solution within the vessel, and the depression in the manometer tube.

Make similar observations on two additional solutions, adding approximately the same amount of solute each time.

At the close of the experiment, rinse the apparatus with solvent (not water), pouring solutions and wash liquid into the " residue jar."

Read the barometer at the start and finish of the experiment.

Obviously, the barometric pressure is p in Raoult's formula; and the depression is $p - p'$.

Observations and Measurements:

Solvent:...........   Solute: ....

Barometer, at start: ....   Corr.: ....

Barometer, at finish: ....   Corr.: ....

Calibration of inner vessel:

  c.c. added: ....

  vol. reading: ....

Manometer rise, pure solvent: ....

	1st Trial	2nd Trial	3rd Trial
Manometer depression:	......	......	......
$p - p'$ (mm. solvent),	......	......	......
$p - p'$ (mm. Hg),	......	......	......
Gms. of solute added:	......		
Total gms. solute:		......	......
Volume reading:	......	......	......
Volume corrected:	......	......	......
Gms. of solvent:	......	......	......
Mol. wt.:	......	......	......

Calculations:

1. Calculate the weight of solvent in the inner vessel for each trial.

2. Calculate the lowering of the vapor pressure for each solution.

3. Calculate the molecular weight of the solute.

EXPERIMENT 15

DISTILLATION WITH STEAM

Object:

To illustrate the principle of steam distillation, and to show that the molecular weight of the less volatile constituent can be determined from the partial pressures of the distilling vapors and the weights of the liquids obtained in the distillate.

Discussion:

Steam distillation is very commonly employed in synthetic chemistry and in chemical technology for separating and purifying high-boiling liquids at temperatures considerably below their boiling points. The process is most successful when the liquid being distilled is non-miscible with water.

The principle involved is the well-known fact that the total pressure exerted by the vapor of a system composed of two non-miscible liquids is equal to the sum of the partial pressures of the individual liquids.

If the liquids are truly non-miscible, there will be a fixed relationship between the respective masses which distil over, so long as there is enough of each of them present to maintain the equilibrium.

By applying the theory of partial pressures to the distillation, it may be shown that

$$\frac{W_A}{W_B} = \frac{p_A \, M_A}{p_B \, M_B}$$

where: W_A and W_B represent the weight of each liquid distilling over in a given time,

p_A and p_B the respective partial pressures at the temperature of the distillation,

and M_A and M_B the molecular weights of the liquids in the vapor state.

75

It is apparent that the method may be used to determine molecular weights of liquids which are not miscible with water. One distils the liquid whose molecular weight is to be determined, with steam, collecting samples of the distillate, and determines the weights of each of the liquids collected. The temperature and pressure are noted. By reference to a table of vapor pressures for water, the partial pressure of water vapor is obtained, and this, subtracted from the atmospheric pressure, gives the partial pressure of the vapor of the liquid whose molecular weight is sought.

Apparatus and Chemicals required:

Steam generator, 1-liter round-bottom flask, still head, condenser, three 100-c.c. graduates, one 10-c.c. pipette, thermometer (50–100° C. in tenths), tripod, 2 iron stands, ring, 2 clamps, 2 burners, corks, rubber tubing; separatory funnel.

Chlorobenzene, bromobenzene, nitrobenzene, or toluene for investigation.

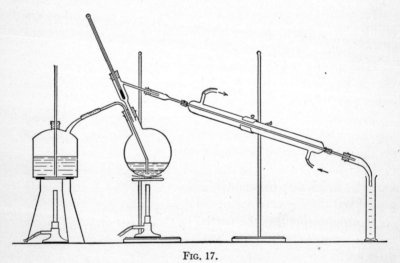

Fig. 17.

Fig. 17 represents the apparatus used for steam distillation. A round-bottom flask inclined at an angle is supported on an iron ring and closed by a two-hole cork. Through one hole passes a glass tube bent downward so as to reach within 0.5 cm. of the bottom of the flask, while the other hole bears the still head which connects the flask to the condenser. A thermometer reading to tenths of a degree is inserted in the still head. Steam is generated in the metal can on the left. This can is provided with a safety tube which reaches to the bottom and extends about 40 cm. above the top.

Method of Procedure:

It is desirable to calibrate each of the 100-c.c. graduates used for collecting samples. The calibration required is twofold: (a) for accuracy of graduation, and (b) for meniscus correction.

The three graduates should be marked A, B and C. Accuracy of graduation is determined by successively adding 10-c.c. portions of water, and noting the reading each time.

The meniscus correction is obtained by running in, say, 30 c.c. of water, adding 10 c.c. of the organic liquid to be used in the experiment, and reading the position of the two menisci.

From the above data, corrections may be obtained which will enable one to determine the true volume of each liquid present at any time.

Half fill the steam generator with water, close the neck by the one-hole cork carrying the safety tube and connect the steam outlet pipe with the round-bottom flask.

Place in the flask 300 c.c. of the organic liquid to be used together with 25 c.c. of water, make all connections tight and see that cold tap water is running through the condenser.

Heat both the can and the flask, the latter by means of a *low* flame which may be removed as soon as the flask is thoroughly heated and the steam no longer condenses in it.

In order to prevent the partial condensation of vapor in the neck of the flask and the still head, wrap a piece of cloth around these parts.

Record the barometric pressure and the room temperature at the beginning and the end of the experiment.

Collect the first 10–20 c.c. of the distillate separately in an Erlenmeyer flask and as soon as the distillate comes over regularly collect three 100-c.c. samples in the graduated cylinders. Watch the temperature carefully during the time of sample taking and record the same every minute, for the distillation should be carried out at constant temperature. This will be the case so long as the steam bubbles through the organic liquid at a uniform rate.

In case the distillates do not separate into two distinct layers at once, it will be necessary to allow them to stand until the next laboratory period before reading the volumes. Inform the instructor if it is necessary to do this.

Disconnect the round-bottom flask, cool and empty its contents into the separatory funnel. Replace the empty flask and pass steam through it, recording one-minute temperature readings until five consecutive constant observations are obtained. Knowing the correct barometric pressure a correction for the boiling points of pure water and the mixture can be applied.

Turn off both gas and water before leaving the laboratory.

Observations and Measurements:

Barometric pressure: 748 .... Corr: ....

Observed boiling point of mixture:

96.8	97.0	98.0	96.1
96.9	97.2	98.1	96.1
97.1	97.5	98.5	......

Observed boiling point of water: 98.6

True boiling point of water: 100

   Thermometer correction: .02 ......

   Corrected boiling point of mixture: 97.6 ......

	Cyl. A	Cyl. B	Cyl. C
Volume of water collected:	96	95.4	96.3
Volume of C₂H₅OH collected:	1.4	13.9	13.

                                                 Total

Corrected volume of water collected: 95 .. ..95.5.. 96 .

Corrected volume of .... collected: 13 ... .

Temperature of water collected: 29

Total weight of water collected: 97.1 .

Total weight of ..... collected: 16.1 ..

Calculations:

1. Prepare a calibration curve for each of the graduates used for collecting distillate.

2. Calculate the weight of each liquid collected (see Table 4.)

3. Determine the vapor pressure of water, and of the organic liquid, at the true boiling point of the mixture.

4. Calculate the molecular weight of the liquid distilled.

EXPERIMENT 16

DISTRIBUTION OF A SUBSTANCE BETWEEN TWO NON-MISCIBLE LIQUIDS

Object:

To determine the partition of benzoic acid between water and benzene, and to test the validity of Nernst's distribution law in this case.

Discussion:

When a solute is shaken with two non-miscible solvents—if it is soluble in each of them—it will distribute itself between the two in accordance with Nernst's distribution law. If the solute is neither associated nor dissociated in either solvent, the partition will take place in accordance with the degree of solubility of the solute in each solvent as follows:

$$K = \frac{C_1}{C_2},$$

where K is the partition coefficient, and
C_1 and C_2 refer to the solubility of the solute in the respective solvents.

If the solute is associated in one of the solvents, say solvent No. 2, and is normal in the other, the formula is modified as follows:

$$K = \frac{C_1{}^n}{C_2}$$

where n is the degree of association, in the second solvent.

In investigating the distribution law, a number of systems may be studied. When succinic acid distributes itself between

80

ether and water, it is found that the solute is normal in both liquids. When benzoic acid distributes itself between water and benzene, the solute is associated in one of the solvents. Many more possibilities are available.

Apparatus and Chemicals required:

Three 150-c.c. separatory funnels, two 125-c.c. Erlenmeyer flasks, one 5-c.c. and one 2-c.c. pipette, 25-c.c. graduate, iron stand with three rings to hold separatory funnels, tripod, Bunsen burner, stock bottle containing approximately N/20 baryta solution connected to a 25-c.c. burette, bottle and burette being fitted with guard tubes.

Bottles containing CO_2-free water, benzene and benzoic acid, phenolphthalein indicator.

Method of Procedure:

Place 25 c.c. of CO_2-free water and 25 c.c. of benzene in each of the three separatory funnels and introduce 1.25, 1.50 and 1.75 grams of benzoic acid, respectively, into the numbered funnels.

Stopper at once and shake for 15 minutes, holding the funnels by the stem and neck in such a manner that the mixture is not warmed by the hands.

Place the separatory funnels in their supporting rings and allow the mixture to separate into two perfectly clear layers.

Analyze the upper (benzene) layer in each of the funnels as follows, taking care not to warm the liquids:

Place 25 c.c. of CO_2-free water and a drop of phenolphthalein in each of the two 125-c.c. Erlenmeyer flasks. By means of the 2-c.c. pipette withdraw and discard a sample from the upper layer in funnel No. 1, then place exactly 2 c.c. of this liquid in each of the Erlenmeyer flasks.

Heat these solutions to boiling and titrate at once with N/20 baryta solution, being careful not to overrun the endpoint. Should the two titrations not check to 0.05 c.c. take further samples and repeat the titrations.

Having analyzed the upper layer in funnel No. 1, analyze those in the other two funnels in like manner.

Carefully draw about 17 c.c. of the lower (aqueous) layer from funnel No. 1, running it into the *dry* graduated cylinder. Rinse the 5-c.c. pipette with this solution, then run exactly 5 c.c. into each of the Erlenmeyer flasks, add 20 c.c. of CO_2-free water and a drop of phenolphthalein to each, heat to boiling and titrate with baryta solution.

After having obtained satisfactory " checks " (to 0.05 c.c.), dry the measuring cylinder and proceed to the analysis of the aqueous layer in the other two funnels.

Before leaving the laboratory, see that the solutions are drained from the separatory funnels. Remove the stopcocks, and leave the funnels supported in their rings so that they will drain and dry before the next laboratory period.

Observations and Measurements:

	No. 1	No. 2	No. 3
Grams of benzoic acid	......	......	......
c.c. of water	......	......	......
c.c. of benzene	......	......	......

Analysis of upper (benzene) layer:

	No. 1	No. 2	No. 3
c.c. of baryta	......	......	......
	......	......	......
	......	......	......
	......	......	......
Mean of constant values	......	......	......
c.c. baryta/c.c. sample T_B	......	......	......

Analysis of lower (aqueous) layer:

	No. 1	No. 2	No. 3
c.c. of baryta	......	......	......
	......	......	......
	......	......	......
	......	......	......
Mean of constant values	......	......	......
c.c. baryta/c.c. sample T_W	......	......	......

Calculations:

1. Express the numerical values of the ratio $\dfrac{T_W}{T_B}$ for the three solutions and see whether a constant value is obtained or not. If not, what conclusion can be drawn?

2. Calculate the ratios: $\dfrac{\sqrt{T_W}}{T_B}$ and $\dfrac{T_W}{\sqrt{T_B}}$.   If either of these is constant what inference can be drawn?

$HAc = .866N$

$NaOH = .1 N$

2. 66 cc of NaOH used to titrate 13 cc of H_2O

$\qquad N_1 V_1 = N_2 V_2$

$\qquad 8.6 \times 1 = 13 \times x$

$\qquad x = .661 N$ of H_2O layer

$\qquad \dfrac{.661}{.205} = 3.22$

BOILING POINTS OF BINARY SYSTEMS (MINIMUM BOILING LIQUIDS)

Object:

To determine the boiling point-composition curve for a pair of miscible liquids evidencing a minimum boiling point.

Discussion:

The boiling points of binary systems of consolute liquids may fall in one of three possible classes:

(a) The boiling point-composition curve lies between the boiling points of the pure constituents.

(b) It drops below the boiling point of either pure constituent.

(c) It rises higher than the boiling point of either pure constituent.

In this experiment, we are dealing with type (b). The boiling points of pure methyl alcohol, pure benzene, and of various known mixtures of the two, are determined, and a curve is plotted from these data.

Apparatus and Chemicals required:

Three-necked boiling-point vessel (or a 500-c.c. " Pyrex " 3-necked distilling flask), condenser, thermometer, iron stand, tripod, ring and clamp.

Methyl alcohol, benzene.

Fig. 18 gives a sketch of the assembled apparatus. The three-necked boiling-point vessel is supported on the wire gauze by means of the perforated asbestos plate (laid on the iron ring) and connected air-tight to the reflux water-cooler on the right. The central opening of the vessel is closed by a tight-fitting perforated cork carrying a thermometer.

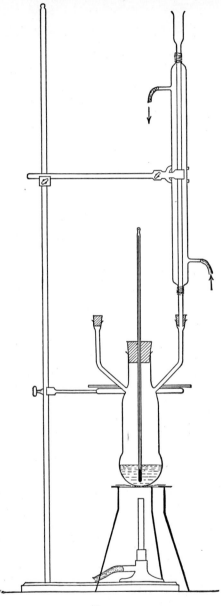

Fig. 18.

Method of Procedure:

Since both benzene and methyl alcohol are highly inflammable it is necessary to insure air-tight connections especially at the one-hole cork connecting the boiling-point vessel to the condenser.

Regulate the flow of tap water through the condenser. Pour 50 c.c. of benzene measured in the 50-c.c. graduate, through the side neck on the left.

Close the neck and determine the boiling point of the liquid. In this and *all* following determinations the bulb of the thermometer should dip *in the liquid* and the thermometer be of such length that the cork does not interfere with readings above 55°.

Record the barometric pressure and room temperature.

Having obtained the boiling point, turn off the gas, wait a few minutes until the liquid has sufficiently cooled, and introduce 10 c.c. of methyl alcohol through the side neck.

Close the neck and determine the boiling point of this mixture. (Shake gently until the alcohol has dissolved.)

Repeat the operation twice by adding successively 20 and 30 c.c. of methyl alcohol.

Disconnect flask from condenser and transfer the solution to the waste bottle. Rinse the flask with about 10 c.c. of methyl alcohol and after assembling the apparatus as before, introduce 50 c.c. of methyl alcohol and determine its boiling point.

Repeat the boiling-point determination three times by adding successively 10, 20 and 25 c.c. of benzene.

Turn off both the gas and water supply and pour the contents of the flask into the waste bottle. Do not rinse the boiling-point vessel with water.

Tabulation of Results:

Barometric pressure: ....mm. Corrected value: ....mm.
Room temperature: ....°
Liquid *A* (benzene)
Liquid *B* (methyl alcohol)

		Boiling point (uncorrected)
A C_6H_6	**B** C_2H_5OH	
50 c.c.		81.6
50 c.c.	Added 10 c.c.	57.2
50 c.c.	20 c.c. (total 30)	57.5
50 c.c.	30 c.c. (60)	58.5
B	**A**	
50 c.c.		68.2
50 c.c.	Added 10 c.c.	63.2
50 c.c.	20 c.c. (total 30)	58.8
50 c.c.	25 c.c. (55)	58.0

Calculations:

1. Compute the volumes of A and B for each mixture, on the basis of a total volume of 100 c.c.

2. Prepare a temperature-concentration diagram by plotting the temperature as ordinate ($10° = 5$ cm.) against the volume concentration (10 per cent = 1 cm.) as abscissa.

3. Construct a smooth curve through these 8 points, designated as P_1, P_2, etc., and locate the minimum on the curve.

4, Construct a second curve, plotting boiling point *vs.* molal composition.

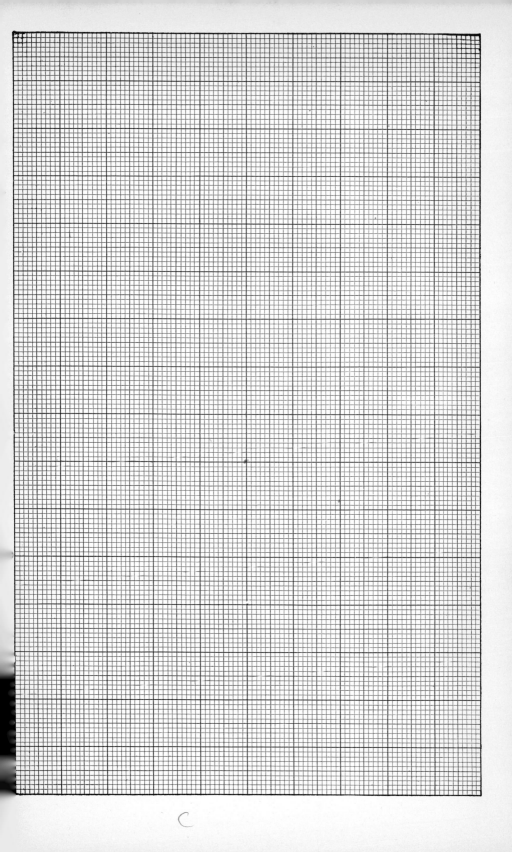

EXPERIMENT 18

BOILING POINTS OF BINARY SYSTEMS. SIWOLOBOFF'S METHOD

Object:

To determine the boiling point-concentration curve for a binary system.

Discussion:

The method proposed by Siwoloboff [1] is particularly well adapted for the determination of boiling points of small samples of pure liquids, and of mixtures. The open end of a short capillary tube (sealed at the other end) is immersed in the liquid under observation. This tube serves as a manometer to enable one to determine the temperature at which the vapor pressure of the liquid is equal to the pressure of the atmosphere.

Apparatus and Chemicals required:

" Pyrex " test tube (50 × 400 mm.) for outer jacket, inner tube (10 × 450 mm.), having a thin walled bulb (20 to 25 mm. diameter) blown at one end, five or six capillary tubes 30 mm. long, sealed at one end, 1-c.c. pipette, thermometer, stirrer, iron stand and clamp, burner.

Benzene-toluene, chloroform-acetone, chloroform-methanol samples in the following proportions by weight: 0–100, 20–80, 50–50, 80–20, and 100–0.

The assembled apparatus is shown in Fig. 19.

Method of Procedure:

Fill the large " Pyrex " test tube two-thirds full of water

[1] Ber., **19**, 795 (1886); O'Dowd and Perkin, Trans. Far. Soc., **4**, 95 (1908); Denslow, Jour. Chem. Educ., **5**, 727 (1928).

(use water-glycerol if the boiling points to be determined are above 100°), fix it in the clamp, and place the stirrer in position.

Dry the sample tube, and fill its bulb half full of liquid A.

Insert the capillary tube in the sample tube with its open end down. Attach the thermometer to the sample tube with rubber bands, taking care that the mercury bulb is at the same level as the bulb of the sample tube. Suspend them in the large test tube as shown in Fig. 19.

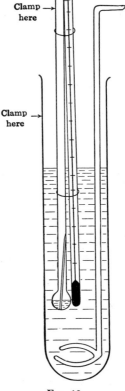

Stirring constantly, warm the jacket throughout by playing a moderate flame over its entire surface; place the burner underneath the tube and closely watch the capillary tube. As the temperature rises in the sample tube, bubbles of air escape from the lower end of the capillary. When the boiling point of the sample is slightly exceeded, a rapid stream of bubbles or vapor escapes. As soon as this is observed, withdraw the flame and allow the bath to cool. Stir constantly. When bubbles no longer issue from the capillary, and the liquid starts to suck back, read and record the boiling point.

Fig. 19.

When the bath has cooled sufficiently, repeat the experiment with the 20–80, the 50–50, the 80–20, and finally the 100–0 sample. Duplicate runs should be made of the 20–80, 50–50, and 80–20 sample since the compositions may have been unduly altered by boiling.

At the conclusion of the experiment, clamp the sample tube in an inverted position and allow it to drain.

Observations and Measurements:

Assigned system *Choloroform acetone*

Atmospheric pressure *753* . . .   corr. . . . . . .

Sample:	Boiling Point:	
A B	1	2
0–100%	*53 4/5*	
20– 80	*55.20*	*55 4/5*
50– 50	*57.4*	*57* . . .
80– 20	*58.6*	*59.2*
100– 0	*60* . . .	

Plotting the Results:

Plot temperature against concentration. Use the second boiling point obtained for the intermediate samples. Indicate which of the three types of curves is found.

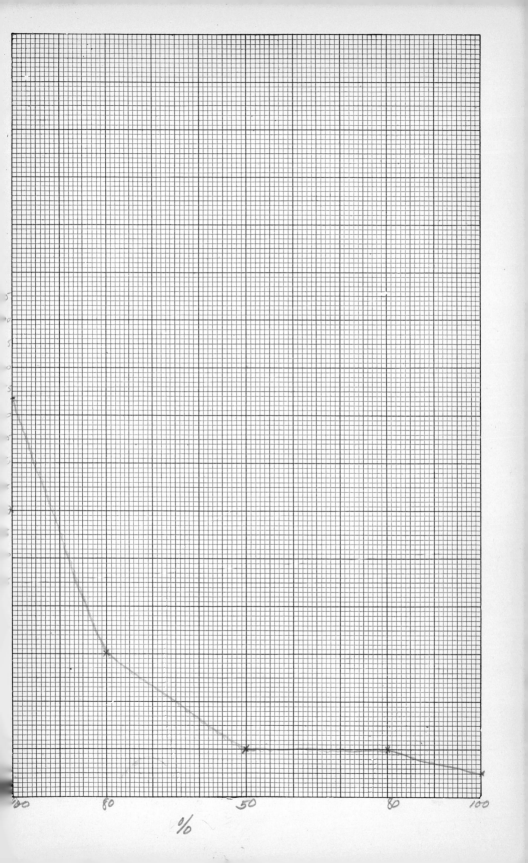

%

EXPERIMENT 19

BOILING POINT—AND VAPOR COMPOSITION CURVE

Object:

To determine the boiling-point curve and the vapor composition curve for a two-component solution.

Discussion:

When a two-component solution is distilled, the composition of the liquid distilled over may in special cases be the same as that left behind in the distilling flask, but ordinarily it is found that the distillate is richer in one component than is the mother liquor.

In the system under consideration, a solution of hydrogen chloride and water, the boiling-point curve belongs to Type C (page 84), viz., a maximum boiling-point type. It is the purpose of this experiment to determine the position of one arm of this curve and to locate the corresponding arm of the vapor composition curve for the system.

In order to accomplish this, a dilute solution of hydrogen chloride is distilled, the temperature being noted from time to time. Immediately following each temperature reading, a sample is drawn from the flask and analyzed in order to obtain the composition of the mother liquor, and a small sample of distillate is taken and analyzed in order to determine its composition. As the experiment proceeds, the boiling point rises and approaches the maximum value for the system, and the composition of the remaining liquor and that of the distillate each approaches the maximum boiling concentration.

In order to locate the other arms of the curves, it would be necessary to start with a strong solution of hydrogen chloride and approach the maximum boiling concentration from the more

94

concentrated side.   This procedure is inadvisable on account of the fact that hydrogen chloride is evolved more rapidly than water.   This requires special equipment to absorb the gas.

Apparatus and Chemicals required:

One-liter distilling flask, condenser, thermometer 100 to 150° C. graduated in tenths, 3 iron stands, 2 clamps, 1 burette holder, 2 test-tube racks with 24 stoppered and labeled test tubes, one 5-c.c. and one 1-c.c. pipette, 100-c.c. graduated cylinder, 150-c.c. Erlenmeyer flask, wash bottle, tripod, wire gauze, two burners, pumice.

Stock bottle containing approximately 10 per cent HCl, stock bottle containing N/5 NaOH, phenolphthalein indicator.

The apparatus is set up as for an ordinary distillation.   The flask should be a long-necked one so that the thermometer held by a tight-fitting cork is completely immersed in the vapor over the scale readings from 100 to 110°.   The bulb of the thermometer should not dip in the liquid but extend about 1 inch below the side neck of the flask.

Method of Procedure:

See that the test tubes in which the samples are to be collected are dry and clean.   They are provided with corks and labeled D_1, D_2, D_3, etc., and R_1, R_2, R_3, etc., in order to distinguish the samples of distillate from samples of residue.

Place 500 c.c. of the 10 per cent solution of hydrochloric acid in the distilling flask with a few bits of pumice stone or glass beads to prevent excessive bumping.   Violent bumping can further be obviated by gently rocking the stand and flask to and fro, thereby swirling the liquid about in the flask.   The use of an asbestos mat or a wire gauze increases bumping and for this reason the distillation should be carried out with a bare flame.

Adjust the flame in such a manner that distillation proceeds rather vigorously, yet at a uniform rate.   As soon as the thermometer has warmed up to equilibrium, i.e., after from 10 to 15 c.c. of distillate have been collected in the graduated cylinder, place the test tube labeled D_1 at the outlet of the condenser and collect about 4 c.c. of distillate.   While this portion is being distilled read the thermometer to 0.1° and record the same.

When enough distillate has been collected, remove the flame, pipette off a 5-c.c. sample of the liquid in the flask (this portion need not be measured accurately) and place it in the test tube marked R_1. Stopper the test tubes immediately.

Replace the thermometer and continue the distillation (using the same flame) at the same rate as before until the thermometer shows a rise of from 0.8 to 1.0°. Reject the portion which has come over during this interval, then collect a 4-c.c. sample of distillate in tube D_2, taking a temperature reading and recording the same as before. Remove the flame and place a 5-c.c. sample from the flask in Tube R_3.

Continue the operation as outlined above, taking (approximately) 4-c.c. samples of distillate and 5-c.c. samples of residue and recording the temperature, for each rise of approximately one degree, until about 10 c.c. of liquid remain in the flask, when a final sample of distillate and residue are taken and the final temperature read.

While one student is carrying out the distillation, his partner determines the HCl contents of the samples by titrating the same with standard (N/5) alkali. The series of R-samples should be cooled to the same temperature as the D-samples before analysis.

The analysis is carried out by withdrawing exactly 1 c.c. of sample by means of the small pipette, running it into a 150-c.c. Erlenmeyer flask, adding about 25-c.c. of boiling distilled water from a wash bottle heated over a wire gauze, and titrating with standard alkali (using two drops of phenolphthalein as indicator) until the first permanent pink color develops. Before taking a sample from a test tube rinse the pipette with the solution to be sampled and remove the last drop of rinse solution from the tip by touching it with a piece of filter paper. Each titration is run in duplicate and the result entered in the record of observations.

When the distillation is complete, rinse the distilling flask, introduce about 250 c.c. of distilled water, assemble the apparatus as before and check the reading of the thermometer at the boiling point of pure water. Record the barometric pressure, then obtain the true boiling point of water at this pressure from Table 2 in the Appendix, and if the thermometer does not read correctly, determine the correction to be applied. Correct all observed temperature readings.

Observations and Measurements:

	Temperatures Observed Corrected		c.c. of alkali used			Normality	Percentage HCl
			Sample 1	Sample 2	Average		
D_1	....	....	....	....	....	....	....
R_1			....	....	....	....	....
D_2	....	....	....	....	....	....	....
R_2			....	....	....	....	....
D_3	....	....	....	....	....	....	....
R_3			....	....	....	....	....
D_4	....	....	....	....	....	....	....
R_4			....	....	....	....	....
D_5	....	....	....	....	....	....	....
R_5			....	....	....	....	....
D_6	....	....	....	....	....	....	....
R_6			....	....	....	....	....
D_7	....	....	....	....	....	....	....
R_7			....	....	....	....	....

Barometric pressure, ...mm. Room temperature ....°
Same corrected ....mm.
Boiling point of water as found ....°
Same as given by table, ...°, Correction: ....°

Calculations:

1. From the result of the titrations find the normality of each sample of distillate and residue, and record the same in the above table.

2. From Table 7 in the Appendix, find the percentage of HCl corresponding to each normality, and place these values in the last column.

3. Plot, on a sufficiently large scale, the percentages so found as abscissæ against temperatures as ordinates. Connect the points by curves and locate the position of the maximum boiling mixture.

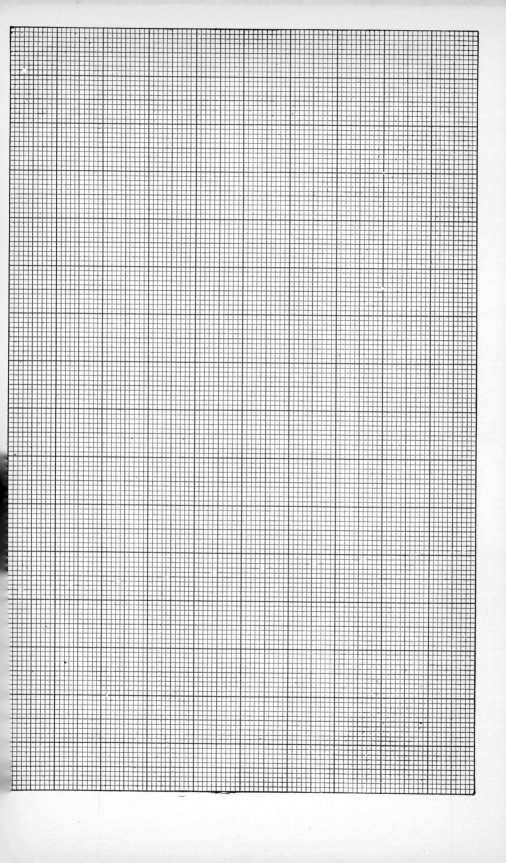

PARTIALLY MISCIBLE LIQUIDS; DETERMINATION OF MUTUAL SOLUBILITY

Object:

To construct the mutual solubility curve for a pair of partially miscible liquids, and to determine their critical solution temperature.

Discussion:

A given pair of liquids may be (a) completely miscible, (b) non-miscible, or (c) partially miscible, at any given temperature. Inasmuch as solubility varies widely with temperature, it may happen that a pair of liquids which are completely miscible at one temperature, may become partially miscible at another, or vice versa.

The system phenol-water furnishes an excellent example of this. Phenol and water are partially miscible at ordinary temperatures, but as the temperature is raised, the mutual solubility is increased. Phenol becomes then more soluble in water, and water becomes more soluble in phenol. When a temperature somewhere between 65 and 70° is attained, the liquids become completely miscible. The temperature at which this happens is known as the critical solution temperature.

There are several methods available for determining the mutual solubility curve for such a pair of liquids. In the one which will be used in this investigation, a number of mixtures of known concentration of the two liquids are prepared, and the saturation temperature for each is determined.

Apparatus and Chemicals required:

Freezing-point tube, jacket for same, thermometer 0–100 C. in $\frac{1}{5}°$, glass stirrer, corks, one 2-liter beaker, one 50-c.c. burette and holder, burner, tripod, wire gauze, iron stand and clamp, one 250-c.c. Erlenmeyer flask.

Phenol, distilled water.

The assembled apparatus is shown in Fig. 20.

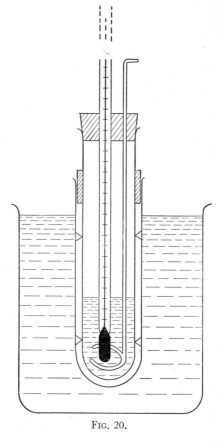

Method of Procedure:

Weigh approximately 10 grams of phenol, and place this amount in the inner tube of the apparatus. Calculate and then add the amount of water required to bring the composition of the system to 70 per cent phenol, 30 per cent water.

Warm the tube until the two layers merge into one, and then place it in the apparatus. Allow it to cool slowly, stirring the liquid vigorously as it cools. Note the exact temperature at which a second liquid phase ap-

Fig. 20.

pears. This will be evidenced by a milky appearance of the liquid.

After a second layer has appeared *on cooling*, slowly warm the system, stirring constantly, and note the temperature at which the liquid clears up.

The temperature found on heating should approximate that found on cooling. With careful work, they may be made to approach each other closely.   The mean is taken as the temperature of saturation.

Now add sufficient water to prepare a 60 per cent mixture, and find its saturation temperature.

Prepare a 50, 40, 30, 20 and 10 per cent solution, and find the saturation temperature for each.

In making the last few solutions, it will be necessary to pour the mixture from the freezing-point tube into a 250-c.c. Erlenmeyer flask, and to add the water to this; otherwise the volume of the tube will not be sufficient to hold the entire mixture.   It will then be necessary to pour the mixture back and forth from the flask to the tube several times, in order to secure a uniform sample.

Observations and Measurements:

Weight of phenol taken: . *10 gms* . . . . . .

		t_1 cooling	t_2 heating
70% mixture; water added: *2.5* . total *7.5*		*47°*	*49°*
60% mixture; water added: *1.1* . total *8.4*		*55°*	*55.1°*
50% mixture; water added: *1.9* . total *10.5*		*61.5*	*63°*
40% mixture; water added: *2.7* . total *12.9*		*—*	*—*
30% mixture; water added: *4.1* . total *16.0*		*64.6*	*64°*
20% mixture; water added: *8.1* . total *21.5*		*64°*	*63.8°*
10% mixture; water added: *2.35* . total *53*		*44*	*44*

Plotting the Results:

Plot the curve of mutual solubilities, temperature *vs.* concentration, and designate the critical solution temperature.

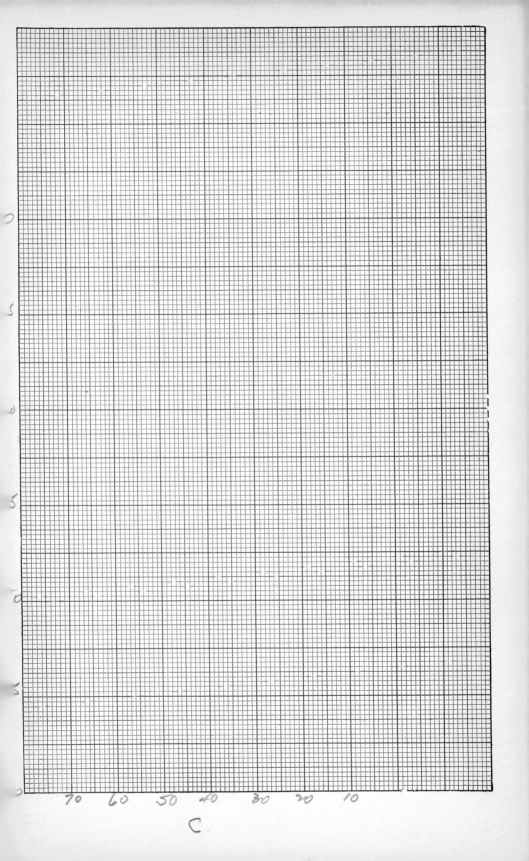

70   60   50   40   30   20   10

C

EXPERIMENT 21

SOLUBILITY CURVE FOR A TERNARY SYSTEM OF LIQUIDS

Object:

To determine the solubility curve for a ternary system of two non-miscible liquids (water and benzene) and a third liquid (acetic acid)[1] consolute with either of the two.

Discussion:

If a given liquid, A, is miscible with each of the two liquids, B and C, B and C being immiscible, it is possible to cause B and C to become mutually miscible by adding different quantities of A to them.

The amount of A needed to cause B and C to become completely miscible is very definite for given concentrations of B and C. When the quantities of A required to render any composition of B–C consolute are determined and plotted on a triangular diagram, the curve obtained shows at once under what conditions the 3 components will form, at the stated temperature, a one- or a two-phase system.

Apparatus and Chemicals required:

One 125-c.c. and one 300-c.c. Erlenmeyer flask, one 2-c.c. and one 5-c.c. pipette, 4 burettes and holders.

Distilled water, benzene, and glacial acetic acid.

Method of Procedure:

(*Student A.*) Using the 5-c.c. pipette, introduce 5 c.c. of benzene into the 125-c.c. Erlenmeyer flask, then add 1 c.c. of water from one burette, and from another burette, little by little, glacial acetic acid until after vigorous shaking a clear

---

[1] Benzene may be replaced by chloroform, if desired, with equally good results.

(non-cloudy) solution is obtained which is saturated with respect to the three components.

Record the volumes added.

Add 2 c.c. of water to the liquid, shake vigorously and repeat the addition of acetic acid until the mixture again becomes homogeneous.

Add successively 3, then 4, 5 and finally 6 c.c. of water and in each case add enough acetic acid to produce a clear liquid. Record all results.

(*Student B.*) By means of the 2-c.c. pipette introduce 2 c.c. of benzene into the 300-c.c. Erlenmeyer flask. Add 25 c.c. of water from one burette and then from a second, enough glacial acetic acid to produce a clear homogeneous liquid after shaking.

The operation is repeated by adding successively 5 more portions of 25 c.c. of water; in each case the exact volume of acetic acid necessary to produce a clear, noncloudy solution is recorded.

Tabulation of Results:

	Benzene	Water			Acetic Acid			Total vol. in c.c.
A_1	5		1			6.0		12
A_2	5	Added 2	Total	3	Added 6.25	Total	13.2	21.2
A_3	5		3	.7	7.90		21.5	....
A_4	5		4	1.0	8.95		28.5	....
A_5	5		5	1.6	9.10		39.6	....
A_6	5		6	2.1	10.13		98.5	....
					39.5			
B_1	2		25					....
B_2	2	Added 25	Total	50	Added 17.7	Total	57.1	....
B_3	2		25	75	6.5		63.6	....
B_4	2		25	100	7.6		71.7	....
B_5	2		25	125	6.5		77.7	....
B_6	2		25	150	....		....	....

Calculations:

1 Assuming that there is no volume change on mixing, compute the volumes of the three components in equilibrium on the basis of having in each case a total volume of 100 c.c.

2. Plot these percentages upon a triangular diagram, indicating the points by A_1, A_2 ....; B_1, B_2 ...., etc. Connect these 12 points by a smooth curve which is to be prolonged by a dotted line ending in the vertices of the triangle, representing 100 per cent water and 100 per cent benzene respectively (it is assumed that benzene and water are completely immiscible).

3. Recalculate the results, expressing the volumes of benzene and water used, in terms of 100 c.c. of acetic acid and plot these data on ordinary cross-section paper.

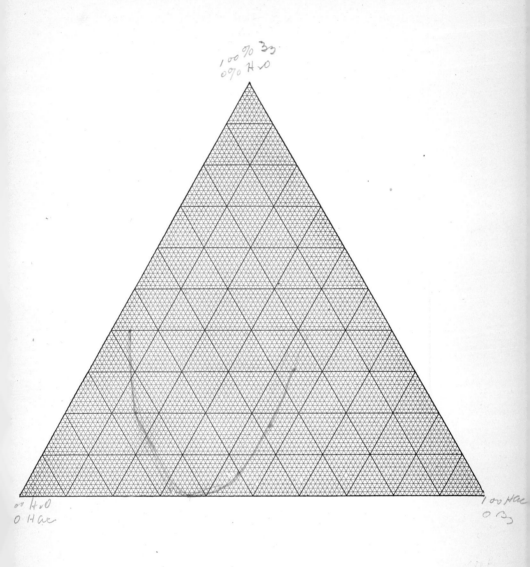

100% 33
0% H₂O

0 H₂O
0 HAc

100 HAc
0 33

EXPERIMENT 22

TRANSITION POINTS IN THE SOLID STATE

Object:

To determine transition points in the solid state by means of cooling curves.

Discussion:

The recognition of the phase rule as a guiding principle in the study of homogeneous and heterogeneous systems has led to the discovery of numerous reversible phase transitions in elements and compounds. In the following experiment the location of two transition points is determined (1) with the aid of an ordinary thermometer and (2) by means of a thermocouple.

A. *Transition Point of Anhydrous Sodium Sulphate*

Special Work:
Findlay's Phase Rule, 3d Ed., p. 341.

Apparatus and Chemicals required:

Iron stand, clamp, iron ring, large copper or iron crucible (dimensions 8–10 cm.), test tube (length 15 cm., diameter 3.5 cm.), Bunsen or Méker burner + rubber tubing, thermometer (0–350°), bottle containing anhydrous sodium sulphate, container with dry sand.

The arrangement is readily understood from Fig. 21. The metal crucible is supported on an iron ring and contains dry sand which completely surrounds the test tube. The thermometer is held in a central position inside the tube by a clamp, in such a way that the bulb is completely immersed in the finely pulverized salt (about 60 grams).

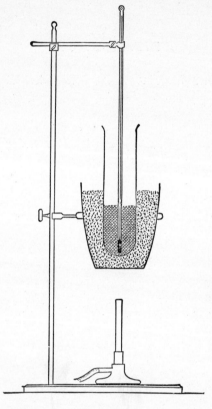

FIG. 21.

Method of Procedure:

Having assembled the apparatus as indicated above the crucible is heated by means of a Bunsen or Méker burner and the temperature of the thermometer registered at intervals of 15 seconds starting from 150° upward.

As soon as the temperature reaches 300°, the gas is turned

off and on cooling the temperature recorded from 300° to 150° at intervals of 30 seconds.

Thermometer Readings:

On heating		On cooling		
150.		300	239.7	199
163.		294.7	236.8	195.2
171.		290.4	237.6	191.5
1837		287	229.	188.2
193.2		282	228.5	182.5
203		278	227.2	179.8
215		273	224.6	176.5
225		270.1	221.8	174.5
233.5		265.6	220.6	169.
242.5		260.8	218.4	165.1
250.2		257.7	215	161
260		254.1	213	158
269.3		250.4	210	157.5
279.		246.7	207	154
287		240	203.6	150.6

Observed transition range:

. . . .

Plotting the Results:

1. Plot the temperature as ordinate against the time as abscissa and indicate by means of an arrow the temperatures of maximum heat absorption and evolution on the heating and cooling curve respectively.

In order to locate inflection points more accurately choose the unit of time on the horizontal axis of such length that the slope of the curve as a whole is under an angle of 45° to horizontal.

Due to the well-known phenomenon of hysteresis these

temperatures do not coincide and the true inversion or transition temperature lies somewhere in between.

B. *Transition Point of Silver Sulphide*

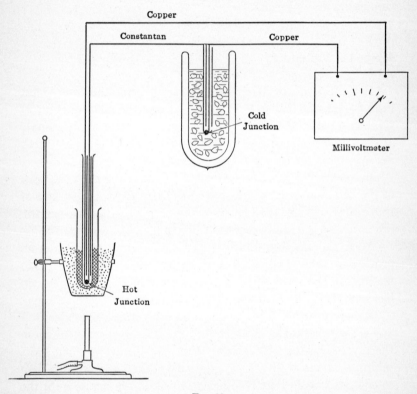

Fig. 22.

Apparatus and Chemicals required:

The same as for A, the thermometer being replaced by a copper-constantan thermocouple and sensitive millivoltmeter, and the tube of anhydrous sodium sulphate by a tube containing about 40 grams of silver sulpide, small Battersea crucible containing about 200 grams of tin, 500-c.c. distilling flask.

The apparatus is sketched in Fig. 22. The thermocouple constructed of thin copper and constantan wires, is protected against short-circuiting by being wound with asbestos or covered by a small clay or " Pyrex " insulator. The hot junction is placed in a protecting tube of " Pyrex," centered in the silver sulphide. The cold junction is inserted in a small Dewar flask containing ice and water.

Method of Procedure:

1. Calibration of the thermocouple. The transition point lies between the boiling point of water and the melting point of tin. It is therefore sufficient to calibrate the thermocouple at these two temperatures. (The melting point of tin is 231.9° C. See Appendix for boiling points of water.)

Insert the hot junction through a perforated cork in the neck of the distilling flask, and fix it about 2 cm. above the surface of the water. With the water boiling, record the barometric pressure and the millivoltmeter reading.

Melt the tin and slowly place the thermocouple and its protecting tube therein. Fix it in a central position. Take readings of the millivoltmeter at 15-second intervals until the tin has solidified. Re-melt the metal and repeat the observations.

Remove the hot junction and the protecting tube; clean off any tin which may have adhered to the tube, and center them in the silver sulphide. Heat slowly to a temperature of about 225°, taking readings at 10-second intervals. Then allow the system to cool, and again take readings at 15-second intervals until the temperature has dropped to approximately 100°.

Observations and Measurements:

Barometric reading ......   Corr. ......
Millivoltmeter reading at the boiling point of water ......
Millivoltmeter readings:

In tin:		In silver sulphide:	
. . . . . .	. . . . . .	. . . . . .	. . . . . .
. . . . . .	. . . . . .	. . . . . .	. . . . . .
. . . . . .	. . . . . .	. . . . . .	. . . . . .
. . . . . .	. . . . . .	. . . . . .	. . . . . .
. . . . . .	. . . . . .	. . . . . .	. . . . . .
. . . . . .	. . . . . .	. . . . . .	. . . . . .
. . . . . .	. . . . . .	. . . . . .	. . . . . .
. . . . . .	. . . . . .	. . . . . .	. . . . . .
. . . . . .	. . . . . .	. . . . . .	. . . . . .
. . . . . .	. . . . . .	. . . . . .	. . . . . .
. . . . . .	. . . . . .	. . . . . .	. . . . . .
. . . . . .	. . . . . .	. . . . . .	. . . . . .
. . . . . .	. . . . . .	. . . . . .	. . . . . .
. . . . . .	. . . . . .	. . . . . .	. . . . . .
. . . . . .	. . . . . .	. . . . . .	. . . . . .

Plotting the Results:

1. Plot the boiling point of water, and the freezing point of tin, in terms of millivolt readings against these two fixed thermometric points. Unite the two points thus obtained by a straight line. This is the calibration curve for the thermocouple.

2. Find the transition temperature for the two solid modifications of silver sulphide, both on heating and on cooling.

PHASE DIAGRAM FOR A TWO-COMPONENT SYSTEM OF METALS

Object:

To construct the phase diagram for a simple binary alloy from cooling curve data.

Discussion:

It is entirely possible to grasp the fundamental principles of phase diagram work by investigating the thermal characteristics of a low melting alloy system by means of ordinary thermometers.

For this purpose the system, tin-lead, or the system cadmium-bismuth, may be used.

The student determines the freezing point of each of the pure metals by means of cooling curves, and locates the temperature of initial solidification and that of final solidification for various mixtures of the two metals in the same manner. The temperature of initial solidification for a mixture is indicated by a sudden change in the slope of the cooling curve, and the temperature of final solidification by a horizontal portion in the cooling curve. The eutectic mixture behaves like a pure metal.

After the cooling curves have been obtained, the points of initial and final solidification are used to plot the phase diagram for the system, the composition of each of the mixtures being known.

Apparatus and Chemicals required:

Two iron stands, 2 iron rings (for holding the crucibles), 2 burners, 2 clamps, two 360° thermometers, 6 numbered Battersea crucibles, size D (6 cm. dia. by 10 cm. long), metallic cadmium, metallic bismuth.

Crucible No. 1 should contain: 200 grams of cadmium.

Crucible No. 2 should contain: 160 grams of cadmium, 40 grams of bismuth.

Crucible No. 3 should contain: 120 grams of cadmium, 80 grams of bismuth.

Crucible No. 4 should contain: 80 grams of cadmium, 120 grams of bismuth.

Crucible No. 5 should contain: 40 grams of cadmium, 160 grams of bismuth.

Crucible No. 6 should contain: 200 grams of bismuth

One unit of the apparatus is shown in Fig. 23. The metal or alloy under observation is placed in a Battersea crucible and covered with a thin layer of charcoal to prevent oxidation. The crucible is supported in an iron ring and heated over a Bunsen burner. The thermometer, covered at the top with a piece of heavy rubber tubing, moves freely through a perforated cork held by a clamp and sinks by its own weight in the metal (or alloy) as soon as the latter fuses.

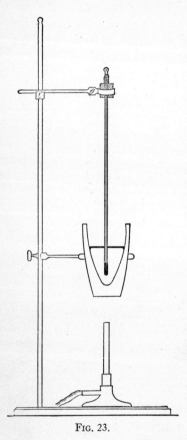

FIG. 23.

Method of Procedure:

Student A confines his observations to samples 1, 2 and 3; student B to samples 6, 5 and 4.

Barely melt the metal in crucible 1(6) and see that the bulb of the thermometer is immersed in the center of the molten metal. Be careful that the mercury does not rise above 360°. If it does tend to rise above this limit, immediately withdraw the thermometer and do not return it to the melt until the temperature has fallen to below 360°.

Naphthalene and p. dichlorobenzene.

Remove the flame, allow the system to cool without interference of any kind (avoid air drafts!) and record temperature readings at 15-second intervals over the range, 340°–120°.

Again melt the metal taking temperature readings from 130°–330°. As soon as the thermometer reaches the latter temperature remove the thermometer.

When the mercury has fallen to below 100° remove any adhering metal by dissolving it in nitric acid in order to prevent a change in the composition of the next melt.

In a similar manner obtain cooling (and heating) curve data for the alloys in crucibles 2 and 3 (5 and 4). In these cases take readings between the limits 300°–120° as the alloys fuse at a much lower temperature than the pure metals.

Observations:

Sample 1 or 6			2 or 5		3 or 4		
On Cooling							
72.1	63.8	56.1	47.8	36.1	33.7	....	....
71.8	63.1	55.5	47.5	35.9	33.4	....	....
71.0	63.0	55.3	47.1	35.7	33.0	....	....
70.8	62.7	54.9	47.0	35.4	32.8	....	....
70.1	67.1	54.6	41.7	55.3	32.5	....	....
69.9	61.8	54.4	41.3	35.1	32.1	....	....
69.6	61.1	54.1	41.2	34.9	32.0	....	....
69.1	60.7	53.8	41.1	34.7	31.8	....	....
68.7	60.3	53.5	40.8	34.5	31.5	....	....
68.3	60.2	53.1	40.4	34.2	31.4	....	....
68.1	59.9	52.7	40.2	34.0	31.2	....	....
68.0	59.1	52.5	39.8	33.8	31.1	....	....
67.5	59.0	52.2	39.5	33.4	30.9	....	....
67.3	58.6	51.8	39.1	33.1	....	....	....
66.9	58.4	51.4	38.7	32.5	....	....	....
66.5	58.1	51.1	38.2		....	....	....
66.2	57.9	50.6	38.0		....	....	....
66.0	57.7	50.4	37.8		....	....	....
65.4	57.3	50.1	37.5		....	....	....
65.1	57.1	49.8	37.3		....	....	....
64.8	56.7	49.5	37.1		....	....	....
64.3	56.5	49.1	36.8		....	....	....
64.1	56.4	48.5	36.4		....	....	....
		48.2					
		48.0					
		47.8					
		47.5					
		47.1					
		46.7					
		46.2					
		45.9					
		45.5					
		45.1					

On Heating ~~Cooling~~

Sample 1 or 6			2 or 5			3 or 4		
75.3	79.9	95.5	66.6	79.1	95.8	....	....	....
75.1	79.0	95.2	66.0	78.3	95.4	....	....	....
74.8	79.0	94.6	65.7	78.0	94.7	....	....	....
74.5	79...	93.6	65.1	77.4	94.1	....	....	....
74.3	79...	92.7	64.8	76.4	93.3	....	....	....
74.1	79...	92.5	64.3	76.0	92.2	....	....	....
74.0	79...	91.9	63.7	75.6	91.6	....	....	....
73.8	79	91...	63.2	74.7	90.8	....	....	....
73.5	79.8	90.7	63.	74.1	90.0	....	....	....
73.3	78.8	90.2	63..	73.7	89.2	....	....	....
73.1	78.8	89.5	63...	73.2	88.6	....	....	....
72.0	78.8	88.3	62.8	72.7	87.6	....	....	....
72.8	78.8	87.6	64...	72.0	87.	....	....	....
72.5	78.5	86.7	64...	71.3	86.1	....	....	....
72.1	76.0	86.0	64...	71.4	85.2	....	....	....
71.8	78...	85.8	64...	70.7	84.1	....	....	....
71.5	78...	84.2	64...	70.3	83.8	....	....	....
71.3	78...	84.2	64...	69.7	83.6	....	....	....
71.0	78...	84.0	64...	69.1	8?.5	....	....	....
69.8	77.2	83.5	64...	68.8	9?.1	....	....	....
	77.5	82.6	63.3	68.5	81.1			
		8?.5	63.3	68.	80.6			
		80.6		67.1	79.7			

Plotting the Results:

1. Plot all three cooling curves on the same sheet of coordinate paper (temperature as ordinate *vs.* time as abscissa), by shifting the time axis successively 2 cm. to the right. Locate for each sample the temperature of initial and final (eutectic) solidification and unite these observations in a table giving for each of the six samples the exact composition and the temperatures of initial and eutectic solidification.

2. Use the data thus obtained for the construction of a complete temperature-composition diagram (plot temperatures vertically and compositions horizontally).

3. On a separate sheet plot the heating curves and see how the breaks in these curves check with those obtained from the cooling curves.

4. In case a metallographic microscope is available, observe the structures of the pure metals, and of the four alloys, on polished and etched samples having the above indicated compositions.

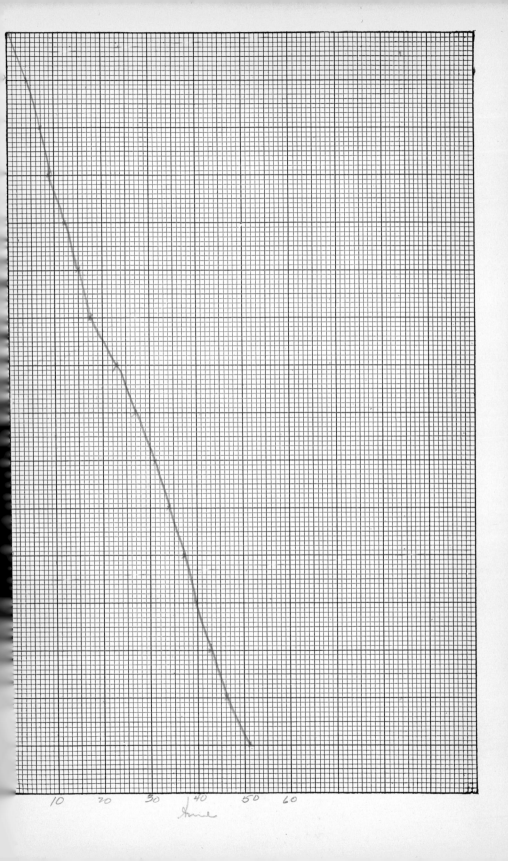

10   20   30   40   50   60

time

MONOMOLECULAR REACTION: DECOMPOSITION OF HYDROGEN PEROXIDE

Object:

To determine the reaction velocity for a monomolecular reaction, viz., the decomposition of hydrogen peroxide.

Discussion:

The simplest type of a chemical reaction is one in which the concentration of but one substance is undergoing change. Hydrogen peroxide decomposes in accordance with the following equation:

$$H_2O_2 = H_2O + \tfrac{1}{2}O_2$$

Its rate of decomposition, normally slow, may be catalyzed by means of colloidal platinum.

If a represents the initial concentration of hydrogen peroxide and x the amount which has decomposed during the time t, then $a - x$ represents the concentration of hydrogen peroxide at the time t. Since the velocity of any reaction at any instant is proportional to the concentration, $v = k(a - x)$. In order to study the velocity of a reaction, it is necessary to express v as $\dfrac{dx}{dt}$. When this value is substituted in the above equation, and the equation is integrated, we obtain:

$$k = \frac{2.3}{t} \log \frac{a}{a - x}$$

Apparatus and Chemicals required:

Thermostat (for ordinary use this may be dispensed with), 50-c.c. burette and holder, iron stand, one 250-c.c. and one 100-c.c. Erlenmeyer flask, one 10-c.c. and one 5-c.c. pipette; one 110-c.c. sugar flask calibrated at the 100- and 110-c.c. marks; one 150-c.c. beaker.

Peroxide solution [1] and colloidal platinum, [2] $N/10$ $KMnO_4$ solution and dilute (1 : 4) sulphuric acid.

Method of Procedure:

Pipette a 10-c.c. sample of prepared hydrogen peroxide solution into a small Erlenmeyer flask, add 5 c.c. of dilute sulphuric acid and titrate with permanganate. Check the titration and record the permanganate required as the " original " permanganate value.

Fill the sugar flask to the 100-c.c. mark with the peroxide solution and then add colloidal platinum to the 110-c.c. mark Record the time and immediately transfer the contents of the flask to the 250-c.c. Erlenmeyer flask.   Keep the solution stirred by shaking the flask.   (If a thermostat is used, the permanganate solution and colloidal platinum should be at the temperature of the bath when they are mixed, and the Erlenmeyer reaction flask should be kept in the bath.)

The progress of the reaction is now followed by titrating 10-c.c. samples at approximately 10-minute intervals. When about 9 minutes have elapsed, pipette a 10-c.c. sample of the reaction mixture into the small Erlenmeyer, add 5 c.c. of dilute sulphuric acid and titrate rapidly with permanganate.   Record the exact time at which the first drop of the permanganate is added.   Inasmuch as the peroxide continues to decompose until all of it has reacted with permanganate, the titration should be continued as rapidly as possible.   Record the volume of permanganate required.

[1] Ordinary 3 per cent peroxide solution is unsatisfactory since it contains a preservative. The solution for investigation should be made by diluting superoxol. The solution should be diluted to such an extent that 10 c.c. will require somewhat less than 50 c.c. of the permanganate solution.

[2] It has been the experience in this laboratory that the most satisfactory method for preparing colloidal platinum for this experiment consists in reducing a 0.01 per cent solution of $PtCl_4$ with carbon monoxide. The solution should be neutralized with potassium carbonate and should contain a trace of agar. Bubble washed carbon monoxide gas through this solution.   A stable colloidal platinum is obtained which usually must be diluted to prevent the peroxide from decomposing too quickly.

Titrate successively 10-c.c. samples of the reaction mixture at approximately 10-minute intervals until 8 samples have been analyzed. In each instance record the time and permanganate volumes as above.

Observations and Measurements:

10 c.c. H_2O_2 solution requires: ....c.c. $KMnO_4$ (original value)

$\dfrac{10}{11} \times$ original value: ....c.c. $KMnO_4$ (zero value $= a$)

Sample	Time in Minutes	c.c. $KMnO_4$ $(a - x)$
1	......	...... *
2	......	......
3	......	......
4	......	......
5	......	......
6	......	......
7	......	......
8	......	......

Calculations:

1. Since the total sample consists of 100 c.c. of peroxide solution in a total volume of 110 c.c., a 10-c.c. sample would have a $KMnO_4$ value, at zero time, equal to 10/11 of the "original" $KMnO_4$ value. Compute and record this as the zero $KMnO_4$ value.

2. Plot the values of $(a - x)$ as ordinate against time in minutes as abscissa.

3. Select two representative points on the curve and calculate the velocity constant for each point.

4. From the curve, determine the exact time when one-half of the peroxide is decomposed.

5. From the integrated equation, compute the time, t, when one-half of the peroxide is decomposed, and compare the result with that obtained in 4.

* $a - x$ equals a at zero time.

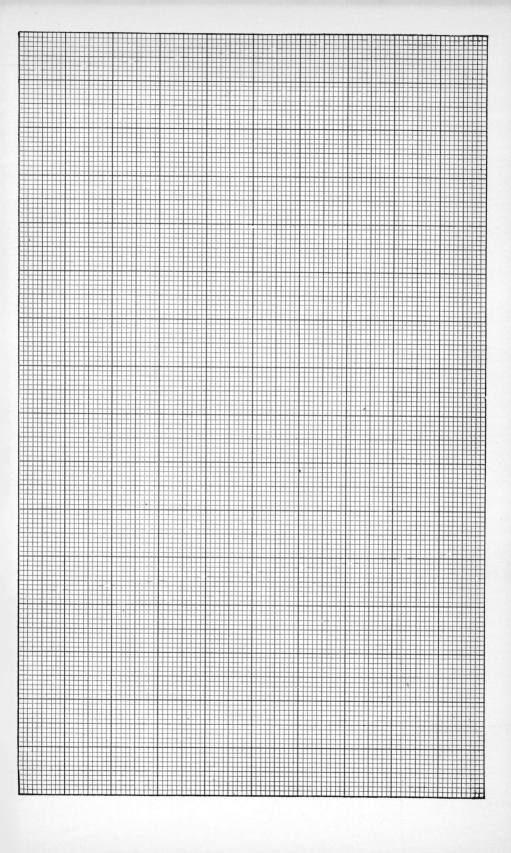

EXPERIMENT 25

MONOMOLECULAR REACTION: INVERSION OF CANE SUGAR

Object:

To determine the reaction velocity for the monomolecular reaction: the inversion of cane sugar.

Discussion:

The inversion of cane sugar furnishes an excellent monomolecular reaction for investigation, owing to the fact that its progress may be followed optically. Solutions of sucrose rotate the plane of polarized light to the right, and equimolecular quantities of glucose and fructose, which are the inversion products, rotate it to the left.

At any instant, the ratio between the change in angular rotation which has been obtained to the total change which will be obtained when the reaction is completed, is the same as that of the quantity of unchanged sucrose present at that instant, to the original amount.

Substituting these values in the integrated equation for a monomolecular reaction:

$$k = \frac{2.3}{t} \log \frac{a}{a - x}$$

we obtain:

$$k = \frac{2.3}{t} [\log (A_0 - A_\infty) - \log (A_t - A_\infty)]$$

where A_0, A_t, and A_∞ are the angular readings at the beginning of the inversion, at time t, and at the end, respectively.

For a description of the polarimeter, the student is referred to any standard textbook on physics or physical chemistry.

Apparatus and Chemicals required:

Polarimeter, with jacketed inversion tube, sodium light, thermostat with pump for circulating constant temperature water through tube jacket, or a coiled copper tube 1 m. long by 5 mm. bore, one 3-necked Woulff bottle carrying thermometer and water inlet and outlet tubes, iron stand, clamp, 2 burners, 25-c.c. pipette, two 100-c.c. beakers; normal HCl, 20 per cent sugar solution preserved by a tiny crystal of camphor.

The polarimeter (drawn schematically), jacketed tube, and sodium light are shown in Fig. 24. Tap water is passed at a regulated rate through a coiled copper tube heated by a carefully regulated flame, next through a one-liter bottle containing the thermometer (not shown in the figure) then through the jacketed polarimeter tube, and thence to waste.

A thoroughly satisfactory source of sodium light [1] consists of a small alundum crucible (R.A. 360) about one-third full of NaCl, heated over a Méker burner.

Method of Procedure:

Bring the water circulating through the jacketed tube to 30° and maintain it there by constant watching.

Dry the polarimeter tube.

Place the sodium flame about 20 cms. from the polariscope, light the gas, remove the tube from its rack, and see that the polariscope is in adjustment.

Place 25 c.c. of the 20 per cent sugar solution in one beaker, and an equal volume (use pipette both times) of normal hydrochloric acid in the other. Bring the temperature of each to 30°, mix the solutions and fill the polarimeter tube, taking care to eliminate any air bubbles which might tend to collect therein.

Place the tube in position and at once take a reading, noting the time at which the reading was taken.

For the first 20 minutes take one-minute readings, for the next 20, two-minute readings and for the next 60, five-minute readings on the polarimeter, recording also time (and temperature).

At the end of 100 minutes, raise the temperature of the

[1] Fales and Morrell, Jour. Amer. Chem. Soc., **43**, p. 1629 (1921).

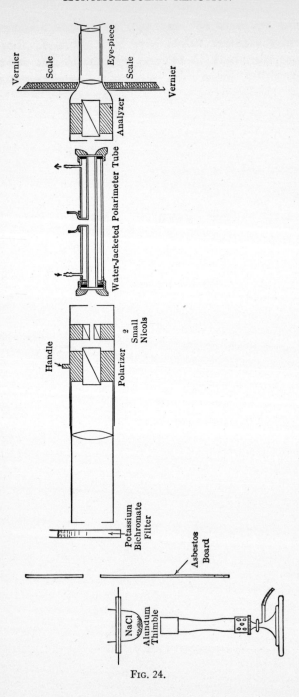

FIG. 24.

circulating water to 65° and take one-minute readings until
5 successive constant values have been obtained; then bring
the temperature back to 30° and continue to take one-minute
readings until 5 consecutive constant values have again been
obtained.   At the temperature of 65° the reaction runs to completion quite rapidly and the values at 30° after complete inversion represent the value A_∞.

Observations and Measurements:

Readings at 30°.

Angle	Time	Temp.	Angle	Time	Temp.
......	......	......	......	......	......
......	......	......	......	......	......
......	......	......	......	......	......
......	......	......	......	......	......
......	......	......	......	......	......
......	......	......	......	......	......
......	......	......	......	......	......
......	......	......	......	......	......
......	......	......	......	......	......
......	......	......	......	......	......
......	......	......	......	......	......
......	......	......	......	......	......
......	......	......	......	......	......
......	......	......	......	......	......
......	......	......	......	......	......
......	......	......	......	......	......
......	......	......	......	......	......
......	......	......	......	......	......
......	......	......	......	......	......
......	......	......	......	......	......
......	......	......	......	......	......
......	......	......	......	......	......

Readings at 65°   Final readings at 30°

Calculations:

1. Plot the observed angles ($1° = 1$ large division) against the times (5 min. $= 1$ large division) as abscissae and draw a smooth curve through the points.

2. Select four representative points on the curve and calculate the velocity constant for these points.

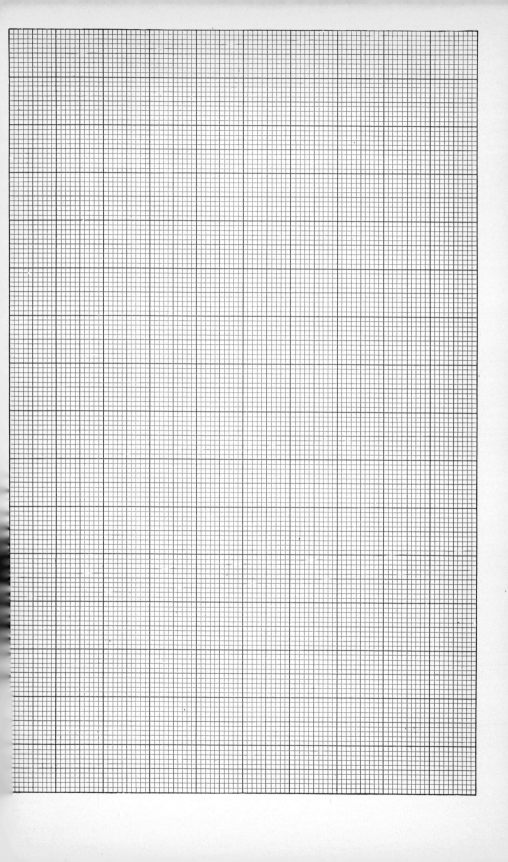

BIMOLECULAR REACTION: SODIUM THIOSULPHATE REACTING WITH ETHYL BROMACETATE

Object:

To determine the reaction velocity for the bimolecular reaction:

$$CH_2BrCOOC_2H_5 + Na_2S_2O_3 = CH_2(NaS_2O_3)COOC_2H_5 + NaBr^1$$

Discussion:

In a reaction of the second order, the concentrations of two substances undergo simultaneous change. The velocity equation for such a reaction is:

$$\frac{dx}{dt} = k(a-x)\cdot(b-x) \tag{1}$$

which, on integration yields:

$$k = \frac{2.3}{(a-b)t} \log \frac{(a-x)b}{(b-x)a} \tag{2}$$

where: k is the velocity constant;

a and b the initial concentrations of the reacting substances;

and x the amount of each which has been consumed in time t.

If a and b were originally equal, the differential equation becomes

$$\frac{dx}{dt} = k(a-x)^2 \tag{3}$$

and this, on integration, gives

$$k = \frac{1}{t}\cdot\frac{x}{a(a-x)} \tag{4}$$

---

[1] Slator, Trans. Chem. Soc., **87**, 484 (1905).

In following the reaction between sodium thiosulphate and ethyl bromacetate one should use such quantities of reagents that the thiosulphate is in excess. The initial concentration of ethyl bromacetate is therefore represented by b, and that of the thiosulphate by a.

Apparatus and Chemicals required:

Thermostat, 2 burettes, 1 double burette holder, iron stand, one 50-c.c., one 25-c.c., and one 1-c.c. pipette, one 125-c.c. Erlenmeyer flask, two 250-c.c. volumetric flasks, one 1-liter flask, one 100-c.c. beaker.

Ethyl bromacetate, N/100 iodine solution, N/60 sodium thiosulphate solution, starch indicator solution.

Method of Procedure:

Pipette about 0.4 c.c. (approximately 15 drops) of ethyl bromacetate into a 250-c.c. graduated flask.[2] Add distilled water, shaking the flask thoroughly to insure solution of the ester in the water. Make up to 250 c.c., and place the flask in the thermostat.

Fill the other 250-c.c. flask to the mark with sodium thiosulphate solution, and place it in the thermostat.

When the temperature of both solutions has reached 25°, the two liquids are mixed in the 1000-c.c. flask (the time of mixing being taken), the flask is shaken, and placed in the thermostat.

At the end of five minutes (counted from the time of mixing) remove 50 c.c. from the reaction flask, and titrate *rapidly* with the hundredth normal iodine solution, using starch as indicator.

At the end of 10, 15, 25, 40, 60, and 90 minutes (from the start of the reaction), withdraw 50 c.c. from the flask, and titrate rapidly as before. Note the time at which iodine solution is run into the titration flask in each instance.

Between the last two titrations, determine the initial concentration of sodium thiosulphate in the flask by withdrawing 25 c.c. from the stock bottle, and titrating with iodine. Why withdraw 25 c.c. here, instead of the 50 taken for the other

---

[2] The ester has strong lacrymatory properties.

titrations? Express this concentration in c.c. of the iodine required.

After at least five or six hours, or better still, at the start of the next laboratory period, titrate 50 c.c. of the liquid remaining in the reaction flask. The reaction being presumably complete at this time, the volume of iodine solution required for this titration represents the excess of thiosulphate originally present in the mixture. The value of this titration, therefore, subtracted from the value of the titration of the 25 c.c. of thiosulphate withdrawn from the stock bottle, gives the initial concentration of the ethyl bromacetate solution present in 50 c.c. of the mixture, expressed in c.c. of iodine solution.

Observations and Measurements:

	Time	c.c. iodine
The solutions were mixed at	....	
1st Sample titrated at	....	....
2d Sample titrated at	....	....
3d Sample titrated at	....	....
4th Sample titrated at	....	....
5th Sample titrated at	....	....
6th Sample titrated at	....	....
7th Sample titrated at	....	....
Titration of 25 c.c. stock thiosulphate		....
Titration of mixture at end of reaction		....

Calculations:

1. Using the integrated equation for the velocity constant of bimolecular reactions, calculate the value of " k " for each sample, expressing the concentration in c.c. of iodine solution used.

2. Also calculate the value of the constant, expressing the concentrations of the reacting mixture in moles per liter.

3. Find the time necessary to convert half of the ester.

4. Plot the concentration of the ester, expressed in c.c. of iodine solution, against the time, and determine from the curve the time necessary to convert half of the ester. Compare the result with that obtained in 3.

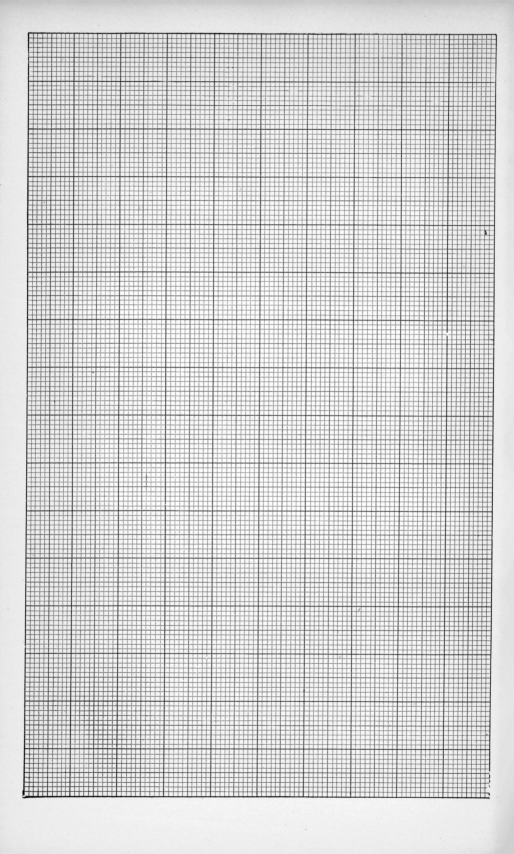

BIMOLECULAR REACTIONS: SAPONIFICATION OF ETHYL ACETATE; CONDUCTIVITY METHOD

Object:

To determine the reaction velocity for the saponification of ethyl acetate, using the conductivity method.

Discussion:

In the saponification of ethyl acetate:

$$CH_3COOC_2H_5 + NaOH = CH_3COONa + C_2H_5OH$$

the progress of the reaction may be followed by titrating the quantities of NaOH present from time to time with standard acid; or it may be followed by observing the change in electrical conductance as sodium hydroxide is consumed and sodium acetate formed.

In this experiment, it is desirable to use equal initial concentrations of the reacting substances. This permits one to use the simplified equation for calculating the velocity constant in which $a = b$.

It is not necessary to determine the constant for the conductivity cell used. If A represents the observed conductance at the start of the reaction, E that at the end and T that at time t (all in reciprocal ohms), the velocity constant is given by:

$$k = 1/t \cdot \frac{x}{a(a-x)} = \frac{1}{t} \frac{(A-T)}{(A-E)[(A-E)-(A-T)]}$$

The student is referred to Experiment 35, page 184, for a discussion of the measurement of conductivity.

139

Apparatus and Chemicals required:

Thermostat, conductivity bridge with accessory apparatus (the conductivity cell should contain at least 50 c.c.), small weighing bottle, 500-c.c. flask, three 25-c.c. pipettes, burette.

0.02 N sodium hydroxide solution, ethyl acetate.

Method of Procedure:

A freshly prepared 0.02 M solution of ethyl acetate should be used. Weigh out about two tenths of a gram of the ester accurately, add the proper quantity of water from a burette to bring the solution to 0.02 M. Place this solution in the thermostat.

Determine the conductance of 0.01 N NaOH by diluting 25 c.c. of the 0.02 N solution with 25 c.c. of distilled water. This value may be taken as the initial conductance of the reaction mixture.

Rinse and dry the conductivity cell. The electrodes may be touched with filter paper, but they should not be touched with anything else.

At an observed time, mix 25 c.c. of the 0.02 M ester and a like volume of the 0.02 N base in the conductivity cell. This marks the start of the reaction.

Measure the conductance as soon as convenient, recording the exact time at which the measurement is made.

Continue to take conductance readings for the remainder of the laboratory period; taking them at 5-minute intervals for the first half hour, and at 10-minute intervals thereafter.

Record the time at which each measurement is made.

The final reading is to be taken at the beginning of the next laboratory period. See to it that the succeeding group does not disturb the apparatus until after this final reading has been taken.

The conductance (in reciprocal ohms) for each reading should be calculated as the experiment proceeds.

Observations and Measurements:

Weight of ethyl acetate taken ......
Volume for 0.02 M solution ......
Time at which the solutions were mixed ......
Conductivity measurements:

	R	a	b	cond.
For 0.01 NaOH	......	......	......	......

For the reaction mixture:

Time	......	......	......	......	......
	......	......	......	......	......
	......	......	......	......	......
	......	......	......	......	......
	......	......	......	......	......
	......	......	......	......	......
	......	......	......	......	......
	......	......	......	......	......
	......	......	......	......	......
	......	......	......	......	......
	......	......	......	......	......
	......	......	......	......	......
	......	......	......	......	......
	......	......	......	......	......

| End | ...... | ...... | ...... | ...... | ...... |

Calculations:

1. Plot observed conductances against elapsed time.

2. From four representative points on the above curve, calculate values for the velocity constant.

3. Determine the time required for the reaction to run half way.

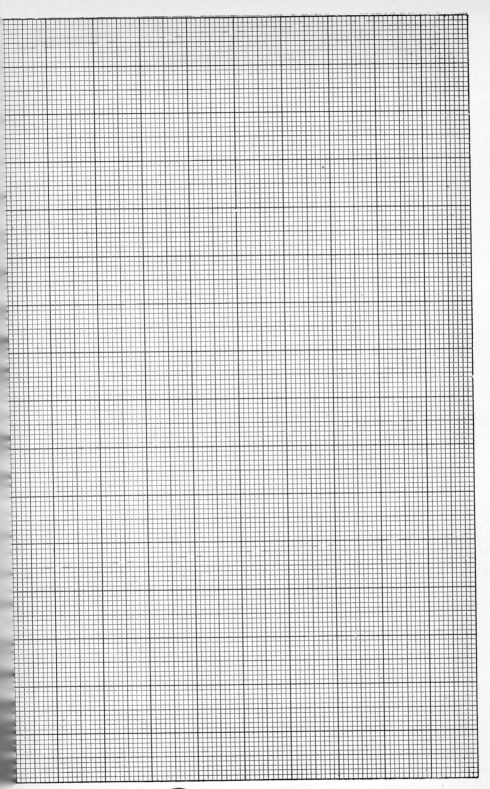

Time.

EXPERIMENT 28

HEAT OF NEUTRALIZATION

Object:

To determine the heat of neutralization of an acid by a base.

Discussion:

The heats of neutralization of strong acids by strong bases, when sufficiently dilute to be completely dissociated, resolve themselves into the heat of formation of water from hydrogen and hydroxyl ion, thus:

$$H^+ + OH^- = H_2O + 13,800 \text{ cal.}$$

If either of the reactants is a weak electrolyte, or if the solution is so concentrated that there is no complete dissociation, the heat of neutralization will differ from the theoretical value given above by the amount of heat required to complete the ionization.

In determining heats of neutralization, one may use the mixture calorimeter shown in Fig. 25 or else two vacuum flasks (a pint and a quart size).[1] The directions given in this experiment apply to a mixture calorimeter.

If vacuum flasks are employed, the quart size is used for containing the base and the mixture, and the pint size for containing the acid before mixing. The water equivalent of the quart flask, together with its thermometer and stirrer, may readily be determined by conducting therein a thermal reaction of known heat evolution, such as a known heat of neutralization or a known heat of solution; or it may be determined by electrical heating as outlined in Experiment 30. The Beckmann thermometer is

[1] J. Ind. Eng. Chem., **18**, 163 (1926).

placed in the large flask and the " ordinary " one in the small flask.

Apparatus and Chemicals required:

Mixture calorimeter (or 1-pint and 1-quart vacuum flask, each fitted with a glass hand stirrer), Beckmann thermometer, ordinary thermometer (0–50° C. in tenths), two 250-c.c. volumetric flasks.

N/4 sodium hydroxide (carbonate free; this solution may be slightly more concentrated), N/4 hydrochloric acid.

The calorimetric vessel is represented in Fig. 25, and consists of a highly polished cylindrical metallic vessel with cardboard or ebonite cover through which pass the Beckmann thermometer, the stirrer, and a glass tube for introducing the solution from the upper vessel. The upper vessel carries a quick-opening valve at the bottom. The calorimetric vessel is surrounded by three other cylindrical vessels and the annular space between the two outer cylinders is filled with water. The upper vessel can be swung into position for discharging its contents into the calorimeter.

Method of Procedure:

Place 250 c.c. of fourth normal sodium hydroxide, accurately measured in one graduated flask, into the (lower) calorimetric vessel. Put the covers, the brass stirrer and the Beckmann thermometer in position, after setting the mercury column so that it reads about half a degree from the bottom of the scale when placed in the alkali solution.

Pour about 260 c.c. of fourth normal hydrochloric acid into the upper vessel, then run it back into the flask.

Make up to exactly 250 c.c. In this way the error due to the acid adhering to the walls of the upper vessel when discharging the 250 c.c. into the calorimeter is eliminated.

Return the accurately measured acid to the upper vessel and place the ordinary thermometer in this solution.

See that both the acid and the base are, when placed in the upper and lower vessel, at approximately the same temperature.

Stirring both solutions, alternately read the two thermometers at 30-second intervals for 5 minutes. Estimate the thousandths of degrees on the Beckmann thermometer by means of a reading glass and the hundredths of degrees on the ordinary thermometer in the same way.

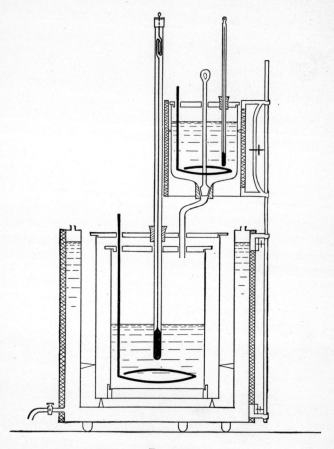

Fig. 25.

At the sixth minute pull the stopper and allow the acid to flow into the alkali. Stirring the mixture constantly, keep on taking readings every minute on the Beckmann thermometer for the next 10 minutes. Record these readings.

Observations and Measurements:

	Readings on Beckmann thermometer (lower vessel)	Readings on ordinary thermometer (upper vessel)
At start	. . . .	
After 30 seconds		. . . .
1 minute	. . . .	
90 seconds		. . . .
2 minutes	. . . .	
150 seconds		. . . .
3 minutes	. . . .	
210 seconds		. . . .
4 minutes	. . . .	
270 seconds		. . . .
5 minutes	. . . .	
6 minutes	. . . .	
7	. . . .	
8	. . . .	
9	. . . .	
10	. . . .	
11	. . . .	
12	. . . .	
13	. . . .	
14	. . . .	
15	. . . .	

Comparison of both thermometers (in lower vessel)

. . . .

. . . .

. . . .

. . . .

. . . .

Weight of calorimeter . . . . . .g.

Weight of brass stirrer . . . .g.

Bulb of Beckmann thermometer immersed.   Weight of water . . . .g.

Weight of water displaced when immersed to same depth as in calorimeter, ...g.

Calculations:

1. From the data secured when comparing the readings of the two thermometers, determine the constant deviation in scale readings for the two instruments. This value, when subtracted from the readings of the ordinary thermometer, converts those into equivalent Beckmann readings.

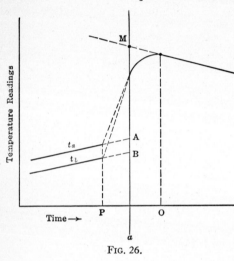

2. Plot temperatures against time, recording all values in terms of the Beckmann scale. By reference to Fig. 26, note the time O at which the maximum temperature was attained after mixing. Midway between O and P (the time of mixing) erect a perpendicular ab, and project the three curves to it.

Fig. 26.

The distance AM represents the true rise in temperature of the acid (dt_A) and BM the temperature rise of the base (dt_B). Since the base was in the calorimeter all the time, dt_B also represents the true rise in temperature of the calorimeter.

Heat liberated by neutralization $= 250\ dt_A + (250 + W)dt_B$, where W is the water equivalent of the apparatus.

3. To obtain the molecular heat of neutralization, apply the following relationship:

$$\text{Mol. heat of neutralization} = \frac{\text{Heat liberated}}{n} \times \frac{1000}{v}$$

where: n is the normality of the weaker solution (acid, usually), and

v is the number of cubic centimeters of acid (or base) used.

Temperature

Time

EXPERIMENT 29

HEAT OF COMBUSTION

Object:

To determine the heat of combustion of a given carbon compound.

Discussion:

When we speak of the calorific value of a substance, we refer to the amount of heat which is liberated when one gram is burned. The heat of combustion refers to the heat liberated when one gram mol. of a substance is burned.

The oxygen bomb calorimeter is the standard apparatus for determining heats of combustion and calorific values. In this device, a weighed quantity of the material under investigation is burned in oxygen, under pressure, and the heat is absorbed by the apparatus itself, and by a known quantity of water surrounding the bomb.

The water equivalent of the calorimeter is usually determined by carrying out a combustion on some substance having a known heat of combustion.

Apparatus and Chemicals required:

Standard combustion bomb calorimeter (oxygen type) with accessories; [1] sample bottles containing pure cane sugar, benzoic acid, and naphthalene for standardization purposes; [2] sample bottles containing organic compounds the heat of combustion of which is to be determined.

---

[1] Inasmuch as complete calorimetric outfits are obtainable from dealers a minute catalogue of equipment is omitted. For careful work the adiabatic calorimeter equipped with vacuum-walled jacket is preferable, but most laboratories would hesitate to use so expensive and fragile an apparatus with beginners. The directions for this experiment are therefore given for a non-adiabatic calorimeter and hold equally well for any of the well-known types of oxygen bomb.

[2] Obtainable from the Bureau of Standards, Washington, D. C. Complete details regarding the standardization of bomb calorimeters are found in Circular No. 11 of the Bureau of Standards.

Fig. 27 and Fig. 28 show views of the Emerson bomb calorimeter which is wiedly used in this country for the determination of the heat value of coke, fuel oil, gasoline, etc.

Method of Procedure:

    A. Determination of the "water equivalent" factor of the apparatus.

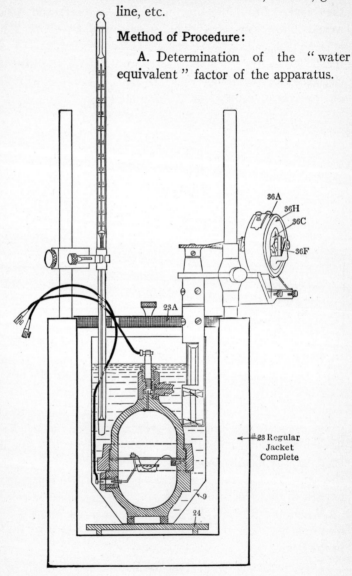

Fig. 27.

By means of a tabloid press, prepare a cartridge containing from 0.75 to 1 gram of benzoic acid, naphthalene or cane sugar.

Weigh this accurately and place it in the small crucible of the bomb. Place the crucible in its support, and attach a weighed iron fuse wire. This wire should be about 2 inches long and be coiled at the center, the coil being directly above the pellet in the crucible. Fasten the ends of the wire to the electrodes by wrapping them tightly. The fuse wire should dip down into, but not touch, the crucible.

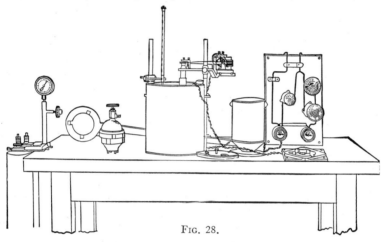

Fig. 28.

Place the outside shell of the bomb in its holder. Carefully place the top in position on the bomb, then screw the two parts together tightly by means of the spanner.

Transfer the bomb to the oxygen fixture and connect the gauge stand to the bomb by screwing up the union. Use the wrench to secure a tight joint. Open the needle valve in the head of the bomb about two turns and carefully " crack " the valve leading from the oxygen cylinder. Do not permit the oxygen to rush from the cylinder or the gauge may be ruined.

When the pressure in the bomb has been increased to 20 atmospheres, close the valve in the cylinder and then the valve in the bomb.

Disconnect the bomb from the fixture and find out by carefully listening for the escape of gas whether there are any leaks.

If no leaks develop, place the bomb within the calorimeter, make the electrical connections and adjust the stirring device.

Using a 500-c.c. graduated flask, add sufficient water to immerse the bomb. (Most calorimeters require 2000 c.c.). It is of the greatest importance that the temperature of this water be about (but not more than) one degree Centigrade below room temperature.

Place the covers in position and clamp the thermometer (which should have a calibration certificate) with its bulb immersed at least 4 inches. In case a Beckmann thermometer is used it should be set so that the mercury thread stands near the bottom of the scale.

After the stirring outfit has been in operation for five or six minutes, take one-minute readings on the thermometer.

When 10 consecutive readings have been obtained, ignite the material in the bomb by closing the firing switch. This should be done exactly on the minute and a note made of the time of firing.

The temperature will rise rapidly during the next few minutes. Continue to take minute readings until at least 15 observations have been made after the maximum temperature is reached and the changes per minute are regular and very small,

When through with the run, remove the bomb, replace it in the holder, and gradually allow the products of combustion to escape through the valve. Unscrew the top of the bomb and note whether the sample was completely burned. Also see whether the iron wire was completely oxidized, or only partly. Any remaining pieces of iron may be collected and weighed and this weight subtracted from the weight of iron taken.

B. Determination of heat of combustion for an assigned carbon compound.

Prepare a tablet containing about 1 gram of the (solid) substance under investigation and weigh it accurately.

Follow the same direction as outlined under A and record the data obtained in the space provided for that purpose.

Carefully clean and dry the bomb before leaving the room.

Observations and Measurements:

A.   Substance used: ...., weight ....g.
       Thermometer used, No.....Room temperature,.....° C.
       Volume of water used ....c.c., temperature of water
       ....° C.

       Weight of iron wire used: ....g.

Time	Temperature	Time	Temperature
....	....	....	....
....	....	....	....
....	....	....	....
....	....	....	....
....	....	....	....
....	....	....	....
....	....	....	....
....	....	....	....
....	....	....	....
....	....	....	....
....	....	....	....
....	....	....	....
....	....	....	....
....	....	....	....
....	....	....	....
....	....	....	....
....	....	....	....
....	....	....	....
....	....	....	....
....	....	....	....
....	....	....	....
....	....	....	....
....	....	....	....
....	....	....	....
....	....	....	....
....	....	....	....
....	....	....	....
....	....	....	....
....	....	....	....

B.   Substance used: ...., weight ....g.

Thermometer used, No. .... Room temperature,
....° C.

Volume of water used ....c.c., temperature of water,
....° C.

Weight of iron wire used: ....g.

Time	Temperature	Time	Temperature
....	....	....	....
....	....	....	....
....	....	....	....
....	....	....	....
....	....	....	....
....	....	....	....
....	....	....	....
....	....	....	....
....	....	....	....
....	....	....	....
....	....	....	....
....	....	....	....
....	....	....	....
....	....	....	....
....	....	....	....
....	....	....	....
....	....	....	....
....	....	....	....
....	....	....	....
....	....	....	....
....	....	....	....
....	....	....	....
....	....	....	....
....	....	....	....
....	....	....	....
....	....	....	....
....	....	....	....
....	....	....	....
....	....	....	....
....	....	....	....

Calculations:

1. Plot temperature *vs.* time.   Project the initial and the final curve to a perpendicular erected midway between the time of firing and the time at which the maximum temperature was obtained (see page 148), and call the intersections on this line the true temperatures before and after ignition.

2. Knowing the heat of combustion of the substance used (benzoic acid, 6320 cal./gm.; cane sugar 3950 cal./gm.; naphthalene 9693 cal./gm. and iron 1600 cal./gm.) calculate the heat liberated by the combustion.   This heat divided by the corrected rise in temperature gives the apparent weight of water of the whole system which, minus the weight of water introduced gives the " water equivalent " of the apparatus.

3. Using the value for the water equivalent found under **2** calculate the heat of combustion for the assigned substances in calories per gram and the molecular heat of combustion in Calories per mole.

4. If the substance used is a fuel, calculate its heating value in B.t.u. per pound.

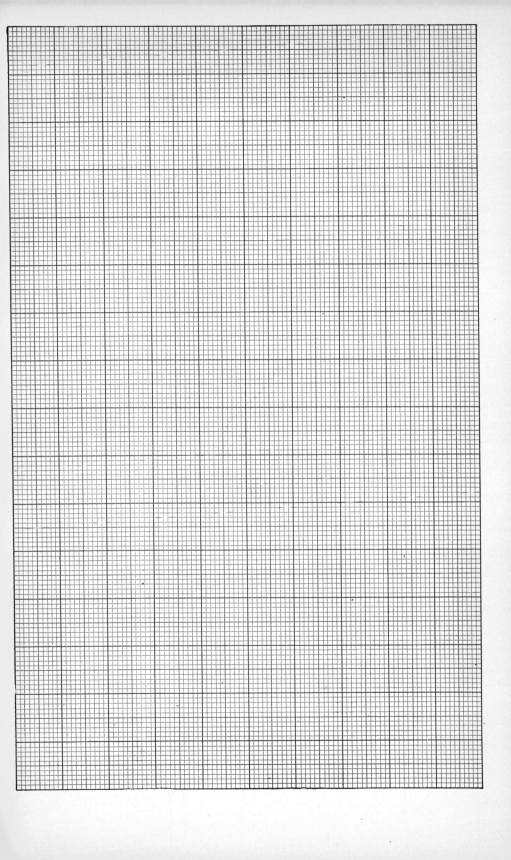

EXPERIMENT 30

HEAT OF SOLUTION

Object:

To determine the heat of solution of a given salt.

Discussion:

Heats of solution may be measured calorimetrically in very much the same way as heats of neutralization. Indeed, the vacuum flask calorimeter described in this experiment may, with slight modification, be used to measure heats of neutralization, heats of solution, heats of reaction, heat of vaporization (see Experiment 31), specific heat, heats of ionization and hydration.

" Heat of solution," as ordinarily measured, is in reality the sum of the heat of solution plus the heat of ionization, if the solute is an electrolyte which is completely ionized at the dilution prepared. It is evident, since degree of ionization depends upon concentration, that the magnitude of the " heat of solution " will depend upon the concentration. It is therefore customary to state the number of mols of solvent in which one mol of solute is dissolved, in publishing heats of solution.

The differential heat of solution is determined at any desired concentration under such conditions that the actual concentration of the solution changes but very little during the determination.

The integral heat of solution is determined by adding solute to pure solvent.

These two heats are identical for very dilute solutions, but they differ widely for more concentrated ones. In this experiment, integral heats of solution will be found.

Heats of solution are usually expressed in calories per mol.

In determining the water equivalent of the calorimeter, one may conduct a thermochemical reaction therein which gives a known heat effect, and calculate the water equivalent; or he may dissipate electrical energy in the apparatus, and calculate the water equivalent from the observed rise in temperature. The formulae used are:

$$q = \frac{RI^2s}{4.183} = \frac{EIs}{4.183} \tag{1}$$

where: q is the heat dissipated in calories,

    s the time in seconds,

    I the current in amperes,

    R the resistance in ohms of the heating element,

and E the voltage drop across the heating coil.

$$q = dt(W + w) \tag{2}$$

where: W is the water equivalent of the apparatus,

    w the weight of water within the calorimeter,

and dt the (corrected) temperature rise.

Apparatus and Chemicals required:

Vacuum calorimeter, as shown in Fig. 29. A one-quart vacuum food container is very satisfactory. The calorimeter should be fitted with a cork for most accurate work. The stirrer may be hand-operated or motor-driven. The heating element should have a resistance of about 5 ohms. Platinum wire should be used for corrosive solutions, although manganin is to be preferred wherever possible on account of its low temperature coefficient of resistivity. Beckmann thermometer, calibrated ammeter 0–1.5 amperes, calibrated voltmeter 0–5 volts, switch, copper wire, 6-volt storage battery, variable resistance, one 250-c.c. volumetric flask, thin-walled test tube.

Various salts for the determinations.

Method of Procedure:

Assemble the apparatus, observing care that the stirrer operates freely and does not strike the walls of the cylinder.

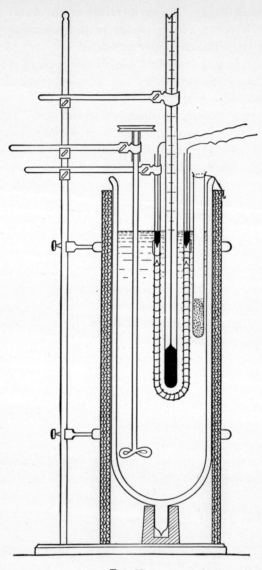

Fig. 29.

Fill the Dewar cylinder with 750 c.c. of water measured out in the graduated flask. The temperature of the water should be about one degree (not more!) below room temperature.

Weigh out sufficient finely powdered salt (assigned for the experiment) to give 1 mol of salt in 200 mols of water, place this amount in the thin-walled test tube and suspend the latter in the water of the vacuum cylinder.

Clamp the Beckmann thermometer in place, after having " set " the mercury thread so that it stands midway on the scale when the bulb is immersed in the water.

Start the stirrer and test the electrical connections by closing the switch for an instant. The current should be equivalent to an expenditure of about 5 watts.

After about 5 minutes commence to record one-minute readings of temperature, and continue until 5 readings of constant difference have been obtained. On the next full minute close the heating switch and record half-minute readings of ammeter and voltmeter and one-minute temperature readings.

Allow the current to pass until the temperature has risen about one degree, stop on the full minute, and remove the copper leads from the mercury cups.

After the current has been interrupted continue the temperature readings for 10 more minutes.

At the end of this period quickly lift the test tube out of the water and shake the salt into the cylinder, noting the exact time at which the transfer was made.

Replace the empty tube immediately and continue the one-minute temperature readings for at least 10 minutes.

Stop the motor and remove the heating coil from the solution.

Observations and Measurements:

Volume of water used ......c.c.   Temperature ....°
Room temperature ....°
Salt used ......, weight of salt ......g.
Resistance of heating coil ....ohms.

Time	Temperature	Current	Voltage
....	....	....	....
....	....	....	....
....	....	....	....
....	....	....	....
....	....	....	....
....	....	....	....
....	....	....	....
....	....	....	....
....	....	....	....
....	....	....	....
....	....	....	....
....	....	....	....
....	....	....	....
....	....	....	....
....	....	....	....
....	....	....	....
....	....	....	....
....	....	....	....
....	....	....	....
....	....	....	....
....	....	....	....
....	....	....	....
....	....	....	....
....	....	....	....
....	....	....	....
....	....	....	....
....	....	....	....
....	....	....	....
....	....	....	....
....	....	....	....
....	....	....	....
....	....	....	....
....	....	....	....
....	....	....	....
....	....	....	....
....	....	....	....

Calculations:

1. Calculate the electrical energy expended in the heating coil and from this determine the number of calories produced.

3. Plot the time-temperature curve on a sufficiently large scale and determine the true rise in temperature caused by the electrical heating. From this rise find the water equivalent of the system.

3. Plot the time temperature curve for the period before and after adding the salt to the water and determine the true change in temperature caused by the solution of the salt. Knowing the water equivalent, find the heat of solution of the salt used.

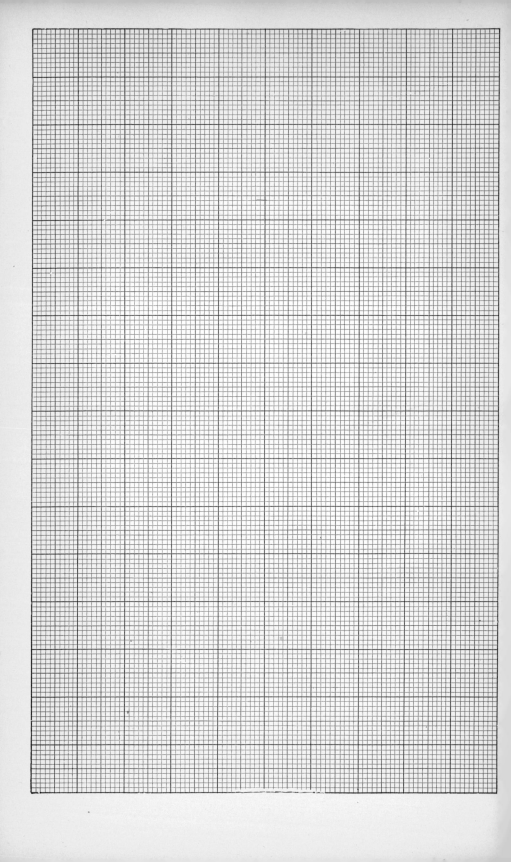

HEAT OF VAPORIZATION. TROUTON'S LAW

Object:

To determine the heat of vaporization for an assigned liquid, to compute its boiling-point constant, and to calculate the constant of Trouton's law.

Discussion:

The latent heat of vaporization of a liquid is defined as the quantity of heat required to change one gram of the substance from the liquid to the vapor state, or vice versa. It is usually determined at the boiling point under a pressure of one atmosphere. The value changes with the temperature, and it is therefore frequently desirable to determine it over a series of temperatures and pressures.

For the precise determination of heats of vaporization, one may use the method developed by Mathews [1] or Kahlenberg's modification of Berthelot's method.[2] Each of these methods requires expensive and delicate apparatus.

The vacuum flask calorimeter may be so modified as to afford a means for determining heats of vaporization, with somewhat less precision than the above methods, but with an accuracy sufficiently high for student work. The liquid under observation is placed within the flask, and is evaporated by the expenditure of a measured quantity of electrical energy. The vapor thus produced is condensed and weighed directly.

The boiling-point constant for the liquid when used as a solvent in boiling-point work may be calculated from the formula:

$$K_b = \frac{0.02T^2}{L_v}$$

[1] Mathews, J.A.C.S., **48**, 562 (1926).
[2] Kahlenberg, Jour. Phys. Chem., **5**, 215 (1901).

where : K_b is the boiling-point constant,

L_v the latent heat,

and T the boiling point in degrees Kelvin.

Trouton [3] discovered the following relationship between the molecular heat of vaporization and the absolute temperature of the boiling point:

$$\frac{ML_v}{T} = 21$$

The above equation has been modified by Nernst and by Bingham to:

$$\frac{ML_v}{T} = 17 + .011T$$

Apparatus and Chemicals required:

One quart vacuum flask calorimeter with tight-fitting rubber stopper through which pass (air-tight): (1) thermometer, (2) heating unit designed to dissipate 30–50 watts coiled at the bottom of the flask, and (3) short delivery tube connected to a condenser; stopwatch, ammeter, voltmeter, control resistance, source of direct current, two 250-c.c iodine flasks, 100-c.c. beaker.

Carbon tetrachloride or other suitable liquid for investigation.

Method of Procedure:

Fill the vacuum flask about two-thirds full of the liquid to be investigated. Assemble the apparatus and adjust the flow of current so that the distillation proceeds at a uniform rate.

After about 50 c.c. of distillate have been collected in the beaker, and the system has reached thermal equilibrium, replace the beaker with a weighed iodine flask and commence to collect condensate. Start the stopwatch at the same instant.

Record temperature, current, and voltage readings every half minute.

When about 75 c.c. of liquid has been collected, remove and stopper the iodine flask, stopping the watch at the same instant, and weigh the flask and contents.

Repeat the procedure, collecting and weighing a second sample.

[3] Trouton, Phil. Mag. (5), 18, 54 (1884).

Observations and Measurements:

Liquid used ...... Barometer ...... Corr. ......
First trial: Wt. flask plus liquid ......
Wt. flask ......
Wt. liquid collected ......

Time	Amperes	Volts	Temperature
....	....	....	....
....	....	....	....
....	....	....	....
....	....	....	....
....	....	....	....
....	....	....	....
....	....	....	....
....	....	....	....
....	....	....	....
....	....	....	....

Calories developed ......

Liquid used ...... Barometer ...... Corr. ......
Second Trial: Wt. flask plus liquid ......
Wt. flask ......
Wt. liquid collected ......

Time	Amperes	Volts	Temperature
....	....	....	....
....	....	....	....
....	....	....	....
....	....	....	....
....	....	....	....
....	....	....	....
....	....	....	....
....	....	....	....
....	....	....	....
....	....	....	....
....	....	....	....
....	....	....	....

Calories developed ......

Calculations:

1. Calculate the heat of vaporization for each trial.

2. From the mean of these two values, compute the boiling-point constant.

3. Calculate the constant in Trouton's Law.

4. Calculate the value of M in the Nernst-Bingham modification of Trouton's Law, and compare it with the simplest molecular weight for the liquid. Does it suggest association or dissociation?

EXPERIMENT 32

ADSORPTION FROM SOLUTION

Object:

To study the adsorption of acetic acid by charcoal, and to determine the constants of the Freundlich adsorption isotherm.

Discussion:

Many cases of adsorption of dissolved substances by solids may be formulated (at least within certain concentration limits), by the equation for the adsorption isotherm proposed by Freundlich:

$$x = k \cdot y^n$$

where: x represents the weight of material adsorbed per unit mass of adsorbing medium,

y the concentration in the solution, at equilibrium,

and k and n are constants under the given conditions.

In carrying out an investigation of this character, one usually brings definite masses of the adsorbent into contact with a series of solutions of the reagent to be adsorbed of varying initial concentrations, and, after equilibrium has been established, he filters and analyzes the various liquids to determine the degree of adsorption in each case. Obviously, the amount adsorbed in each instance is equal to the initial minus the final concentration.

The adsorption curve is plotted from these data.

The equation for the adsorption isotherm may be written in the logarithmic form as follows:

$$\log x = \log k + n \log y$$

When $\log x$ is plotted against $\log y$, a straight line will be obtained if the equation holds for the case under investigation.

171

The constants k and n are taken from the intercept, and the slope of the line thus obtained.

Apparatus and Chemicals required:

Six stoppered 125-c.c. flasks, six 125-c.c. Erlenmeyer flasks, one 50-c.c. volumetric flask, burette and holder, one 10-c.c. pipette, filter stand, 2 funnels, two 100-c.c. beakers, filter paper.

Blood charcoal, approx. 0.4 N acetic acid (23 c.c. of glacial acetic acid made up to 1 liter) N/10 alkali, phenolphthalein.

Method of Procedure:

Into each of the six stoppered flasks, labeled 1 to 6, place exactly 5 grams of charcoal.[1]   Place in each flask 50 c.c. of acetic acid solution, made up (in the volumetric flask) as follows:

No. 1 stock solution of acetic acid (approx. 0.4 N).

No. 2   25 c.c. of acetic acid plus water.

No. 3   15 c.c. of acetic acid plus water.

No. 4   7.5 c.c. of acetic acid plus water.

No. 5   4 c.c. of acetic acid plus water.

No. 6   2 c.c. of acetic acid plus water.

Do not neglect to rinse the volumetric flask with water each time.

Shake each sample for at least 5 minutes, care being taken to keep them all at the same (room) temperature.

Filter the solutions and collect the filtrates in properly labeled flasks.   These solutions are now analyzed for acetic acid, by titration with NaOH, 10-c.c. samples being used for solutions 1 and 2;   20-c.c. for 3 and 4;   and 40-c.c. for 5 and 6.

Care must be observed in titrating numbers 5 and 6, for they do not require much reagent, and there is not sufficient solution left for another sample.

Also titrate 10 c.c. of the stock acetic acid.

[1] Inasmuch as different samples of charcoal exhibit wide variations in adsorbing power, it is desirable for the instructor to determine the proper quantity to use, and advise the students before they begin the experiment.   Blood charcoal is recommended.

Observations and Measurements:

Variety of charcoal used ..*horita*..

Quantity used *2.6 c.c.*

Volume of solutions, initial, 50 c.c.

Titrations of solutions:

Stock Bottle	No. 1	No. 2	No. 3	No. 4	No. 5	No. 6
	10	*10*	*20*	*20*	*40*	*40*
34.31	*46.5*	*18.31*	*18.1*	*6.1*	*6.01*	*.67*
......	......	......	......	......	......	......

Average: ....

Calculations:

1. From the analysis of the stock solution, and the dilutions made in preparing the six solutions, calculate the volume of base which would have been required to neutralize the acid initially present in each of the six flasks, and record this volume as the " initial concentration," in the accompanying table.

2. From the titration of each filtered solution, and the ratio between the total volume placed in the stoppered flask to the volume of sample titrated, calculate the volume of base which would be required to neutralize all the acid left in solution in each flask, after adsorption had taken place. Record this as " final concentration."

3. Initial concentration minus final concentration equals amount adsorbed. Let " final concentration " equal y, and amount adsorbed, x.

4. Plot y against x and draw the adsorption isotherm.

5. Plot log y against log x, and ascertain the values of k and n from the curve so obtained.

Flask No.	Tabulation of Results		x Amt. Adsorbed	Log x	Log y
	Initial Conc. (c.c. of base)	y Final Conc. (c.c. of base)			
1	*34.31*	*23.36*	*10.95*	....	....
2	*17.16*	*16.56*	*.60*	....	....
3	*10.73*	*8.28*	*1.45*	....	....
4	*5.34*	*2.76*	*2.58*	....	....
5	*2.65*	*1.01*	*1.64*	....	....
6	*1.31*	*.18*	*1.13*	....	....

FLOCCULATION OF SUSPENSOIDS BY ELECTROLYTES

Object:

To determine flocculation values for a negative (or positive) suspensoid sol, using electrolytes having cations (or anions) of different valence, in order to test the validity of the Schulze-Hardy rule.

Discussion:

The flocculation value of a suspensoid sol represents concentration of electrolyte (in millimols per liter) necessary to precipitate the sol completely after a stated interval of time. The volume used for computing the concentration is the *total* volume of sol + added electrolyte. The values obtained for the negative As_2S_3-sol with salts having mono-, di-, and tri-valent cations can be related to the actual number of millimols adsorbed by the flocculated colloid. These values, according to Freundlich, should be in the ratio of 3 : 2 : 1. If these numbers are plotted against the flocculation values 3 points of an adsorption isotherm should be obtained. To such a curve applies the well-known equation (see Experiment 32):

$$x = ky^n \tag{1}$$

where: x is the amount of material adsorbed per gram of adsorbent,

y is the concentration of the adsorbed substance in the solution,

and k and n are constants.

In its logarithmic form this equation becomes:

$$\log x = \log k + n \log y \tag{2}$$

which is a straight line relationship. If one plots, therefore, log 3, log 2 and log 1 against the logs of the corresponding flocculation values, the points obtained should lie on a straight line.

Apparatus and Chemicals required:

Four burettes and holders, 2 test-tube racks, twenty-five 50-c.c. " Pyrex " test tubes, 10-c.c. pipette, 2000-c.c. Erlenmeyer flask, CO_2 generator, H_2S generator.

0.2 M NaCl (11.7 gm. per l.), 0.005 M $BaCl_2$ (1.22 gm. $BaCl_2 \cdot 2H_2O$ per l.), 0.0005 M potash alum solution (0.237 gm. $KAl(SO_4)_2 \cdot 12H_2O$ per l.), amorphous arsenic (As_2O_3).

Method of Procedure:

Boil about 5 grams of As_2O_3 for 10 minutes with 200 c.c. of distilled water, filter the hot solution into a 2-l. Erlenmeyer flask and dilute the filtrate to 1000 c.c.

Pass a rapid stream of H_2S (hood!), washed by bubbling through water, into the solution until the opalescent liquid becomes turbid and remove the excess of H_2S by bubbling a stream of CO_2 through the sol. Filter the sol before use.

Thoroughly clean all test tubes, and carefully steam them.

From 2 burettes containing distilled water and the stock solution of NaCl run into 5 numbered test tubes 8, 6, 4, 2 c.c. of water and 2, 4, 6, 8 and 10 c.c. of NaCl solution.

In 5 other numbered test tubes pipette 10 c.c. of the As_2S_3-sol, and to each of these add in turn the corresponding dilute NaCl solution. In each case mix the sol and the electrolyte *in exactly the same manner* by inverting the stoppered tubes twice, *without vigorous shaking*. After 15 minutes' standing (for more accurate work 2 hours are taken) each tube is once more inverted, and after standing for 5 minutes more the samples are examined against a dark background.

Take the lowest concentration at which a clear solution appears above the settling precipitate as the (approximate) flocculation value.

In order to fix this value more accurately, start another series of 5 test tubes with smaller variations in concentration than previously employed and operate as before.

Follow the same procedure for the other two electrolytes, and find their flocculation values. These values, which should be in the neighborhood of 50, 0.75 and 0.09, respectively, depend somewhat on the concentration of the sol. (If time permits, determine the flocculation values again for a sol having $\frac{1}{5}$ of the previous concentration.)

Observations and Measurements:

NaCl		BaCl$_2$		AlK(SO$_4$)$_2$	
c.c. used	in m-mols	c.c. used	in m-mols	c.c. used	in m-mols
....	....	....	....	....	....
....	....	....	....	....	....
....	....	....	....	....	....
....	....	....	....	....	....
....	....	....	....	....	....
....	....	....	....	....	....
....	....	....	....	....	....
....	....	....	....	....	....
....	....	....	....	....	....
....	....	....	....	....	....

Flocculation values   ....

Plotting the Results:

1. Plot the flocculation values and the corresponding ordinates 3, 2, and 1.

2. Plot log 3, log 2, and log 1 against the logarithms of the flocculation values and see whether the values obtained lie on a straight line.

EXPERIMENT 34

SOLUBILITY PRODUCT

Object:

To determine the solubility product for a sparingly soluble electrolyte, and to investigate the influence of common ions, and complex formation, on its solubility.

Discussion:

Case I. Determination of the solubility product.

Silver bromate is a sparingly soluble salt.[1] When a saturated solution is prepared at room temperature, the dissolved portion is almost completely dissociated.

$$AgBrO_3 = Ag^+ + BrO_3^-$$

If one expresses the solubility of the salt in mols per liter, it is evident, if the dissolved portion is completely dissociated, that the concentrations of silver and bromate ions will be identical with the solubility.

$$S = C_{Ag^+} \cdot C_{BrO_3^-} = x^2 \qquad (1)$$

where: S is the solubility product,
and x the ionic concentration.

Case II. Solubility of $AgBrO_3$ in the presence of $AgNO_3$.

When a saturated solution of silver bromate is prepared in the presence of an electrolyte which produces a common silver ion, the solubility is lowered, in accordance with the following mass law equation:

$$S = (C_{Ag^+} + C'_{Ag^+})(C_{BrO_3^-}) \qquad (2)$$

where: C'_{Ag^+} is the concentration of silver ion originating from dissociation of the added electrolyte,

[1] Getman, 4th Ed., l.c.p. 513; Noyes and Sherrill, l.c.p. 168; Reedy, J.A.C.S., **43**, 1442 (1921).

and C_{Ag^+} is that originating from the dissolved silver bromate. Since

$$C_{Ag^+} = C_{BrO_3^-} = x_1$$

$$S = (x_1 + C'_{Ag^+})x_1 \tag{3}$$

Case III. Solubility of silver bromate in the presence of sodium bromate.

$$S = C_{Ag^+}(C_{BrO_3^-} + C'_{BrO_3^-}) \tag{4}$$

where: $C_{BrO_3^-}$ is the concentration of bromate ion originating from the dissolved silver bromate,

and $C'_{BrO_3^-}$ is that originating from the dissociation of the added sodium bromate. Since

$$C_{Ag+} = C_{BrO_3^-} = x_2$$

$$S = x_2(x_2 + C'_{BrO_3^-}) \tag{5}$$

Case IV. The solubility of silver bromate in the presence of the complex-forming ion: ammonium.

In the presence of ammonium hydroxide, silver bromate forms a soluble complex double salt in accordance with the following equation:

$$AgBrO_3 + 2NH_3 = Ag(NH_3)_2BrO_3$$

this dissociates as follows:

$$Ag(NH_3)_2BrO_3 = Ag(NH_3)_2^+ + BrO_3^-$$

Since the silver in this complex cation is not available for depressing the solubility of silver bromate, we may write the following expression for the solubility of the bromate:

$$S = C_{Ag^+}(C_{BrO_3^-} + C'_{BrO_3^-})$$

where: C_{Ag^+} and $C_{BrO_3^-}$ are the ionic solubilities coming from the dissolved silver bromate, and

$C'_{BrO_3^-}$ is the ionic concentration coming from the ionization of the complex. Since

C_{Ag^+} is equal to $C_{BrO_3^-}$ we will denote these by x_3, whence

$$S = x_3(x_3 + C'_{BrO_3^-})$$

Note: In this experiment, it will be assumed that the degrees of dissociation of all the electrolytes involved are 100 per cent. For work of the highest accuracy, the actual degrees of dissociation should be used. These are, for the concentrations employed: silver bromate in water, 95 per cent, and for silver bromate, and the other salts in Cases II, III, and IV, 90 per cent.

Apparatus and Chemicals required:

Thermostat, fitted with horizontal rotator for solubility work, five 4-ounce oil-sample bottles, one 50-c.c. pipette, cotton filters for same, six 125-c.c. Erlenmeyer flasks, burette and holder.

Pure silver bromate, 0.01 N sodium bromate, 0.01 N silver nitrate; 0.02 N ammonium hydroxide; N/20 KCNS, saturated ferric ammonium sulphate solution, nitric acid.

Method of Procedure:

Clean the five oil-sample bottles thoroughly, dry them, and place one gram of silver bromate (weighed approximately) in each. Then make the following additions:

To No. 1, 75 c.c. of cold distilled water.
To No. 2, 75 c.c. of hot distilled water.
To No. 3, 75 c.c. of 0.01 N $AgNO_3$.
To No. 4, 75 c.c. of 0.01 N $NaBrO_3$.
To No. 5, 75 c.c. of 0.02 N NH_4OH.

Stopper the bottles carefully, and label them. Shake bottle No. 2 vigorously for 5 minutes.

Place the bottles in the thermostat, and let them run several hours. Whenever possible, this preliminary part of the experiment should be performed the day preceding the one on which the analyses are to be made.

Standardize the KCNS solution against the 0.01 N $AgNO_3$, as follows: Withdraw a 50-c.c. sample of the silver nitrate, and run it into 25 c.c. of distilled water in an Erlenmeyer flask. Add 5 c.c. of ferric ammonium sulphate solution, 5 drops of nitric acid, and titrate to a faint permanent pink.

Analyze the solution in each bottle in the same manner. In withdrawing samples, stop each bottle in turn with its neck protruding above the water in the bath, and remove the cork. Fit a cotton filter to the 50-c.c. pipette, and fill the pipette to some point above the mark. Remove the filter, adjust the volume to the mark, and run the sample into a marked Erlenmeyer flask.

In analyzing bottle No. 5 (Case IV) it must be remembered that titration with KCNS evaluates the silver present in the complex ion $Ag(NH_3)_2{}^+$ as well as the silver in the simple ion Ag^+. The known amount of $Ag(NH_3)_2{}^+$ must be subtracted from the total silver found to give the amount of Ag^+ present.

Observations and Measurements:

> Standardization of KCNS   . . . .
>
>   . . . .
>
>   . . . .
>
> Mean . . . . . .   Normality . . . . . .

Case I.

> Titration of bottle No. 1 . . . . . .
> Titration of bottle No. 2 . . . . . .
>
>   Mean . . . . . .
> C_{Ag^+} . . . . . .

Case II.

> Titration of bottle No. 3 . . . . . .
>
> $(C_{Ag^+} + C'_{Ag^+}) =$

Case III.

> Titration of bottle No. 4 . . . . . .
>
> $C_{Ag^+} =$

Case IV.

> Titration of bottle No. 5 . . . . . .
>
> $(C_{Ag(NH_3)_2{}^+} + C_{Ag^+}) =$

Calculations:

1. Calculate the solubility product for silver bromate, from the data in Case I.

2. From the solubility product obtained above, and from the known concentrations of $AgNO_3$, $NaBrO_3$, and NH_4OH used in Cases II, III and IV, calculate the concentration of Ag^+ coming from the dissolved $AgBrO_3$ in each case, and compare these results with the amount of Ag^+ which was found by analysis in each case.

CONDUCTIVITY AND DEGREE OF IONIZATION

Object:

To determine degree of dissociation by the conductivity method, and to verify Ostwald's dilution law for weak electrolytes.

Discussion:

Electrical conductance of solutions is usually measured by a modification of Wheatstone's bridge, in which the battery is replaced by a source of high-frequency alternating or interrupted direct current, such as a buzzer, induction coil, or oscillator, and the galvanometer by a sensitive telephone receiver.

The following relationship holds for a conductivity bridge set up as indicated in Fig. 30 (on p. 187):[1]

$$a : b = R : x$$

where: a and b are the lineal distances each side of the contact on the slide wire,

R is the known resistance in the left arm of the circuit,

and x is the resistance of the electrolyte in the cell.

The conductance of the solution, c is the reciprocal of its resistance

$$c = \frac{1}{x}$$

The specific conductance, L, of a solution is defined as the conductance of one centimeter cube of that solution taken between

[1] The location of telephone and induction coil as shown in the figure should preferably be interchanged.

parallel electrodes each one centimeter square, separated from each other by a distance of one centimeter.

It is evident that it would be extremely difficult to secure and maintain a conductivity cell which would fulfill the requirements for the measurement of specific conductance. For this reason, conductances are usually measured in calibrated cells of varying size, for which the " cell constants " are known.

The cell constant is the factor by which the observed conductance in a given cell is multiplied, to obtain the specific conductance. It is determined by measuring the conductance of a solution of known specific conductance, such as $N/50$ KCl, and dividing this specific conductance by the observed conductance.

The equivalent conductance of a solution Λ is the conductance of one equivalent of solute. It is obtained by multiplying the specific conductance by the volume in cubic centimeters required to contain one equivalent.

$$\Lambda = Lv$$

Equivalent conductance approaches a maximum value with increased dilution. This maximum value Λ_∞ is sometimes called the " equivalent conductance at infinite dilution " and represents the sum of the individual ionic conductances involved.

The Ostwald dilution law is an application of the law of mass action to ionization. It is valid only for weak electrolytes:

$$K = \frac{\alpha^2}{(1 - \alpha)v}$$

where: K is the ionization constant,
      α the degree of dissociation,
and v the volume in liters required to contain one equivalent of the solute.

Apparatus and Chemicals required:

Thermostat, kept at 25° C. to 0.1°; conductivity cell, conductivity bridge consisting of slide wire, resistance box, microphone hummer, telephone head-set, and necessary wiring, one 10-c.c. pipette calibrated to contain, 10-c.c. pipette " to deliver."

N/50 potassium chloride, conductivity water,[1] N/16 acetic, benzoic, succinic or other weak acid (or base) for investigation.

Method of Procedure:

It is important that the position of the electrodes be not altered during the course of the experiment; nor must the platinum black surfaces of the electrodes be touched so as to change their character in any way.

Pour out any liquid which may be in the cell and rinse it, together with the electrodes, three times with fiftieth-normal KCl solution, using a few c.c. at a time. The electrodes are best rinsed by gently moving them up and down in the cell a few times.

After thorough washing, introduce 10 c.c. of the fiftieth normal KCl solution, place the cell in the thermostat and determine the conductance of the solution at 25°. See that a minimum on the telephone is obtained with the point of contact near the middle of the bridge wire.

Record a, b and R.

The value of the cell constant is obtained by dividing the specific conductance of fiftieth-normal potassium chloride at 25° (see Table 9) by the observed conductivity as determined above.

Remove the KCl solution, rinse the cell and electrodes with conductivity water and dry them by touching with filter paper.

By means of the 10-c.c. pipette calibrated *to deliver*, introduce 10 c.c. of the sixteenth-molar acid assigned for observation and determine its conductivity at 25°.

Add to the solution in the cell by means of the 10-c.c. pipette calibrated *to deliver* 10 c.c. of CO_2-free distilled water; thoroughly stir the resulting mixture by moving the electrodes

---

[1] Ordinary distilled water is usually not satisfactory for conductivity work on account of the dissolved gases which it contains. If the laboratory distilled water has a specific conductance greater than 3×10^{-6} mhos, it should not be used.

Conductivity water is most readily prepared by treating acidified distilled water for several hours with potassium permanganate, followed by redistillation, using a tin or a "Pyrex" glass condenser. The first runnings should be rejected. The water should be protected against the gases of the laboratory.

gently up and down; then withdraw 10 c.c. by means of the 10-c.c. pipette calibrated *to contain* and discard the portion taken out.

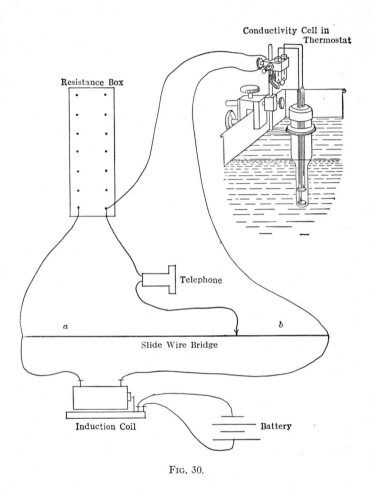

Fig. 30.

Measure the conductivity of the thirty-second molar solution of acid thus obtained.

Proceeding as above, dilute the solution in the cell progressively to $M/64$, $M/128$, $M/256$ and $M/512$ and determine the conductivity each time.

When finishing the experiment, either leave the last solution in the cell or fill it with distilled water.

Do not leave the cell dry.

Observations and Measurements:

Determination of cell constant using N/50 KCl.

Bridge reading, left ...... right ...... $R =$ ......ohms

Assigned acid: ....

Bridge reading	M/16	M/32	M/64	M/128	M/256	M/512
Left:	....	....	....	....	....	....
Right:	....	....	....	....	....	....
Resistance (R)	....	....	....	....	....	....

Calculations:

1. Calculate the cell constant.

2. Compute the conductance, specific conductance and equivalent conductance for each dilution of acid.

3. From Table 10 obtain the value of the equivalent conductance at infinite dilution of the acid used and then calculate the degree of ionization at each concentration.

4. Calculate the constant of Ostwald's dilution law for each dilution.

5. Plot specific and equivalent conductances, also the degrees of ionization against volumes as abscissae.

6. Tabulate the values found in the following table:

Assigned weak acid ....

	M/16	M/32	M/64	M/128	M/256	M/512
Obs. conductance:	....	....	....	....	....	....
Spec. conductance:	....	....	....	....	....	....
Equiv. conductance:	....	....	....	....	....	....
Degree of ioniz.	....	....	....	....	....	....
Ionization const.	....	....	....	....	....	....

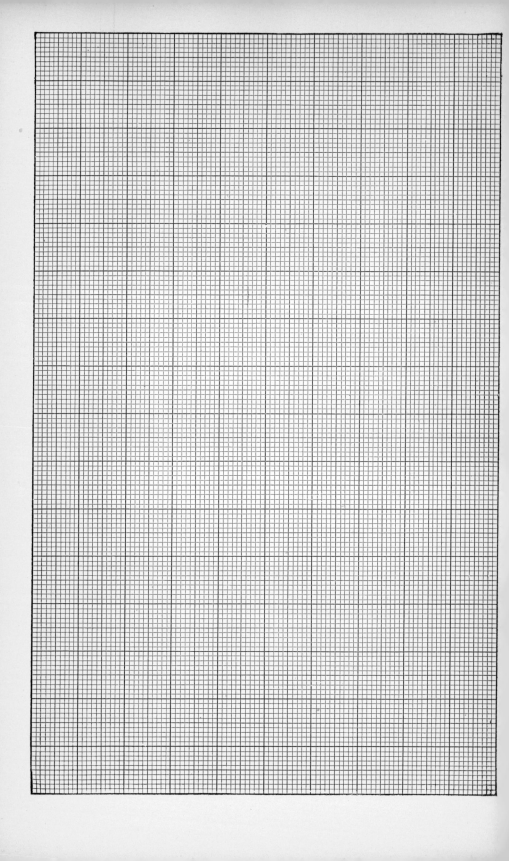

EXPERIMENT 36

HYDROLYSIS. CONDUCTIVITY METHOD

Object:

To determine degrees of hydrolysis, and the hydrolysis constant for aniline hydrochloride, using the conductivity method.

Discussion:

When a salt of a weak acid or base is dissolved in water, hydrolysis occurs. The degree of hydrolysis may be determined from conductivity measurements.

Aniline hydrochloride hydrolyzes to form phenyl ammonium hydroxide, a very weak base, and hydrogen chloride, a strong acid.

$$C_6H_5NH_3Cl + H_2O \rightleftharpoons C_6H_5NH_3OH + HCl$$

In dilute solution, the hydrogen chloride is practically 100 per cent ionized. The phenyl ammonium hydroxide is in equilibrium with aniline and water in accordance with the equation:

$$C_6H_5NH_3OH \rightleftharpoons C_6H_5NH_2 + H_2O$$

The degree of hydrolysis, x, is calculated in the following manner:

Let Λ_s represent the equivalent conductance of aniline hydrochloride under conditions such that no hydrolysis has taken place, Λ_h the equivalent conductance when hydrolysis has taken place to a degree x, and $(\Lambda_A + \Lambda_B)$ the equivalent conductance if the salt were completely hydrolyzed. Then:

$$x = \frac{\Lambda_h - \Lambda_s}{(\Lambda_A + \Lambda_B) - \Lambda_s}$$

191

Λ_h is measured directly, Λ_s by forcing back the hydrolysis on the addition of an excess of aniline. Λ_A and Λ_B representt he equivalent conductances of the acid and base formed.

Since phenyl ammonium hydrochloride is an extremely weak base, one usually neglects the small value of Λ_B. The equivalent conductances of hydrochloric acid at 25° C. at dilutions of 32, 64, and 128 liters are, respectively, 393, 399, and 401 mhos.

The hydrolysis constant K_h is calculated as follows:

$$K_h = \frac{K_{\mathrm{BOH}}}{K_{\mathrm{H_2O}}} = \frac{(1-x)v}{x^2}\frac{\alpha_s}{\alpha_a}$$

where: K_{BOH} is the ionization constant for the weak base,
and α_s and α_a are each practically equal to unity, and may be dropped out.

$$K_{\mathrm{H_2O}} = 0.82 \times 10^{-14} \text{ at } 25° \text{ C.}$$

Apparatus and Chemicals required:

Thermostat, conductivity apparatus (see Experiment 35), four 10–c.c. pipettes, labeled " aniline," " aniline hydrochloride," " aniline hydrochloride in aniline," and " water."

M/32 aniline, M/32 aniline hydrochloride, M/32 aniline hydrochloride in M/32 aniline, conductivity water, M/50 KCl solution.

Method of Procedure:

The success of this experiment depends absolutely upon the avoidance of contaminating one solution with another. Use the proper pipette for each solution.

Determine the " cell constant " as directed in Experiment 35.

Measure the conductance of aniline hydrochloride at dilutions of 32, 64, and 128 liters, using conductivity water for making the dilutions.

Measure the conductance of aniline hydrochloride in M/32 aniline, at dilutions of 32, 64, and 128 liters, using M/32 aniline for making the dilutions.

Observations and Measurements:

Cell constant: a...... b...... R......

Aniline hydrochloride in water

	$M/32$	$M/64$	$M/128$
a	......	......	......
b	......	......	......
R	......	......	......

Aniline hydrochloride in aniline:

a	......	......	......
b	......	......	......
R	......	......	......

Calculations:

1. Calculate the cell constant.

2. Calculate the equivalent conductance for each of the six measurements.

3. Calculate the hydrolysis constant K_h.

4. Calculate the ionization constant K_{BOH} for phenyl ammonium hydroxide.

EXPERIMENT 37

TRANSPORT NUMBERS [1]

Object:

To determine the transport numbers of the ions Ag^+ and NO_3^-.

Discussion:

The transport number of an ion is defined as the ratio of the quantity of electricity carried by that ion to the total quantity carried by both anion and cation. The transport numbers of two given ions are proportional to the velocities of their ionic migrations.

$$n_a = \frac{v}{u + v} \qquad\qquad n_c = \frac{u}{u + v}$$

where: n_a and n_c are the transport numbers of anion and cation, and v and u are their velocities of ionic migration, respectively.

Since transport numbers are proportional to ionic migrations, they are usually determined from observation on the changes in concentrations in a three-compartment electrolytic cell.

In determining the transport numbers of Ag^+ and NO_3^- a dilute solution of silver nitrate, of known concentration, is placed in the cell and electrolyzed between silver electrodes. A coulometer in series with the cell enables one to determine the quantity of electricity which has passed. Electrolysis should not be continued long enough to produce any change in concentration in the middle compartment.

[1] The minimum time required for the completion of this experiment is about 3 hours.

After electrolysis, the solutions are withdrawn from the anode and cathode compartments, and carefully analyzed for silver.

Basing the calculations upon data secured from the anode solution, one very carefully determines the number of equivalents of silver c_2 in that compartment after electrolysis. Knowing the initial concentration of the silver nitrate solution, he is able to calculate the number of equivalents of silver c_1 originally present. There will be an increase which we will call i equivalents; $c_2 - c_1 = i$. It is obvious that there is also an increase of i equivalents of nitrate ion in this compartment.

During the electrolysis, Ag^+ has been produced from the silver anode. The amount can be calculated from data secured in the coulometer. Call the quantity of silver-ion thus produced m equivalents, then $m - i = p$, the number of equivalents of Ag^+ which have migrated out of the anode compartment. We have seen that i equivalents of NO_3^- migrated into the anode compartment.

Hence

$$n_{Ag^+} = \frac{p}{i+p} = \frac{p}{m} \quad \text{and} \quad n_{NO_3^-} = \frac{i}{i+p} = \frac{i}{m}$$

One may similarly base his calculations on data secured from concentration changes in the cathode compartment.

Apparatus and Chemicals required:

Transport number cell with silver electrodes, copper coulometer, ammeter 0–1 amp., adjustable resistance, source of direct current at least 32 volts, switch, copper wire, 2 iron stands, 2 clamps, burette and holder, four 250-c.c. Erlenmeyer flasks, crucible tongs, 25 c.c. pipette, 50-c.c. graduate, wash bottle.

Copper coulometer solution,[1] 0.05 N $AgNO_3$, standard KCNS (1 c.c. = 0.005 gm. Ag) saturated ferric ammonium sulfate indicator solution containing sufficient HNO_3 to suppress hydrolysis, alcohol, distilled water.

The apparatus is shown (partly schematically) in Fig. 31. A three-compartment cell as given in the sketch is preferable

---

[1] Copper coulometer solution may be prepared by dissolving 150 grams of $CuSO_4 \cdot 5H_2O$ in 1 liter of water, and adding 28 c.c. of concentrated sulphuric acid, and 60 c.c. of ethyl alcohol.

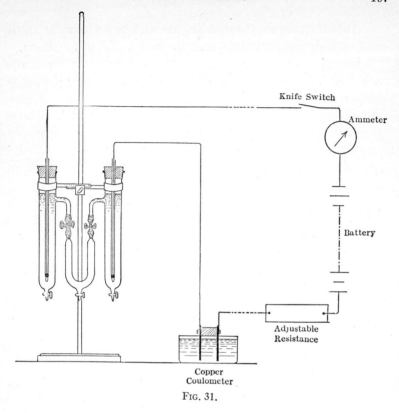

Knife Switch

Ammeter

Battery

Adjustable
Resistance

Copper
Coulometer

FIG. 31.

for the use of beginners, as it offers less opportunity for the
introduction of errors in drawing off the contents of the various
compartments at the end of
the run. A simple and efficient
copper coulometer may be
made from a small crystal-
lizing dish about 2 inches in
diameter, and 2 square sheets
of copper, held in position

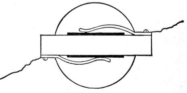

FIG. 32.

by brass spring clips attached to a hardwood electrode
holder, which rests on the dish, as shown in Fig. 32. This
construction provides a convenient means of holding the electrodes and does away with the necessity of terminals soldered
to the copper sheets. With the three-compartment cell a

potential of 32 volts is required to furnish the necessary current.

Method of Procedure:

Wash the coulometer cathode with distilled water, then with alcohol. Grasp it with the crucible tongs, and ignite the alcohol adhering to it. The cathode will be warmed sufficiently by the burning alcohol to dry it completely. When it is cool, weigh it accurately to a tenth of a milligram.

After weighing the cathode, clean and dry the two stoppered flasks, marked A and M, and weigh the one marked A to 0.01 gm.

While the first student is carrying out the operations directed above, the second should clean and dry the cell, fill it with stock silver nitrate solution, and assemble the apparatus, observing care that the electrical connections are made as per the diagram.

Nearly fill the coulometer with coulometer solution, and adjust R to give its maximum resistance.

Close the switch, noting the time, and adjust the resistance to give a current of between 0.01 and 0.02 ampere. The duration of passage of current should be two hours. During this time, the strength of the current should be held constant.

At the conclusion of the electrolysis, interrupt the current, noting the time, carefully close the pinch-cocks, and withdraw the contents of the anode compartment into stoppered Erlenmeyer marked A, rinsing the compartment and the anode with a small amount of the original solution from the AgNO$_3$ stock bottle. Open the pinch-cock next to the anode compartment, and withdraw the contents of the middle compartment into the flask marked M, but do not rinse this compartment.

Remove the cathode from the coulometer, rinse it with water, then alcohol, and dry and weigh as before.

Weigh flask A, with its contents, to 0.01 gm.

While the first student is weighing the flask and cathode, the second should determine the concentrations of silver in the AgNO$_3$ solution in the stock bottle, and in the solution in flask M, by titration with standard KCNS, as follows:

Rinse the 25-c.c. pipette with a small portion of the solution to be analyzed, discard this portion, then withdraw a 25-

c.c. sample of the solution, run it into a 250-c.c. Erlenmeyer flask, add 50 c.c. of distilled water, and 1 c.c. of ferric ammonium sulphate solution, then run standard KCNS in from the burette until the first permanent red tint is obtained. Check the result by a second titration.

If the concentrations of Ag^+ in the stock bottle and in the solution from the middle compartment do not agree, diffusion has taken place, and the results will be inaccurate.

After weighing, analyze the solution in flask A in like manner.

Before leaving the apparatus, see that the clamps and stopcocks are open, so that the cell will drain.

Pour the coulometer solution back into the proper stock bottle.

Observations and Measurements:

1 c.c. standard thiocyanate solution equivalent to
....gms. Ag^+
Time of starting electrolysis ....
Time of stopping electrolysis ....
Current strength used ....
Weight of copper cathode after electrolysis ....
Weight of copper cathode before electrolysis ....
Cathode gain   ....
Weight flask A plus solution   ....
Weight flask A ....
Weight anode solution   ....
Titrations: c.c.
   Stock solution   ....
                               ....
                        Ave. ....
                               ....
Middle compartment   ....
                        Ave. ....
Anode compartment   ....
                               ....
                        Ave. ....

Calculations:

1. From the weight of copper deposited in the coulometer, calculate the weight of silver dissolved from the anode.

2. From the total weight, and the analysis, of the anode solution, calculate the amount of Ag^+ actually found in the anode compartment, assuming that the density of the dilute solution is unity.

3. From the analysis of the stock solution calculate the quantity of Ag^+ originally present in the anolyte, assuming as before that its density is unity.

4. From the data obtained in 1, 2, and 3, calculate the transference numbers of the two ions.

ELECTROMOTIVE FORCE MEASUREMENTS: CONCENTRATION CELLS

Object:

To measure the electromotive force of concentration cells, to determine the concentration of a $AgNO_3$-solution, and to measure the solubility of $AgCl$.

Discussion:

The Potentiometer:

For the precise measurement of electromotive forces under such conditions that the cell undergoing investigation will neither become polarized nor suffer an apparent lowering in E.M.F. due to " RI drop," the potentiometer is perhaps the most satisfactory instrument available.

This instrument consists essentially of a very uniform resistance wire wound on a drum, and supplemented by unit coil resistances in series with the wire. It is so designed that when current of a definite value is passed through its circuit, there is a definite drop in potential along the wire and across the coils. The resistance of each coil is usually made equal to that of the bridge wire. By manipulating a selector switch, which enables one to tap into the circuit between any two given coils, and by moving a contact on the drum wire, which taps at any point along that wire, one is able to obtain potentials accurately from zero to the maximum value for the instrument, with a precision greater than 0.1 millivolt, depending upon the type of instrument at hand.

In using this device, unknown electromotive forces are determined by balancing them against the known drop produced along the potentiometer. Before making a reading, the value of the current within the potentiometer circuit is adjusted to the proper value. This is done by connecting a standard cell (of known E.M.F.) in place of the source to be measured, setting the instrument for this known E.M.F., and adjusting the value of the potentiometric current by means of external uncalibrated resistances until a galvanometer in series with the standard cell gives a zero reading.

Single Potentials:

The single potential between a metal and a solution of one of its salts may be calculated from the Nernst equation:

$$E = \frac{RT}{nF} \log_e \frac{P}{p} \tag{1}$$

where: E is the single potential,
R the gas constant 8.316 joules/degree,
n the valence of the ion,
F the value of the Faraday 96,500 coulombs,
p the osmotic pressure,
and P the electrolytic solution pressure.

In the measurement of single potentials, it is necessary to employ two electrodes: (1) the electrode under consideration, and (2) an electrode of known E.M.F. The calomel electrode is widely used for this purpose, its electromotive force being 0.3375 volt when filled with tenth normal KCl; 0.2830 with normal; and 0.2488 with saturated KCl; all at 20° C. When using a calomel electrode, the potential measured is the algebraic sum of the single potential under consideration, and the potential of the calomel electrode.

Concentration Cells:

A cell composed of two electrodes of the same metal, one dipping in a more concentrated, the other in a less concentrated solution of a salt of the metal is called a concentration cell. For such a cell:

$$E = \frac{v}{u + v} \cdot \frac{2 \times 0.058}{n} \log \frac{\alpha_1 C_1}{\alpha_2 C_2} \tag{2}$$

where: $\dfrac{v}{u+v}$ is the transport number of the anion (0.53 for

$\qquad$ AgNO$_3$),

$\qquad$ n the valence of the cation,

$\qquad$ C_1 and C_2 the respective concentrations

and $\qquad$ α_1 and α_2 the degrees of dissociation of the salt in the two solutions.

Utilizing the above equation (2) one may determine: (a) the degree of ionization in a given solution, knowing the value in its companion solution; (b) the ionic concentration in a solution of unknown strength; (c) the solubility of a sparingly soluble salt.

Apparatus and Chemicals required:

Potentiometer, standard cell, 1–10000 ohm protective resistance, galvanometer, calomel cell, 5 silver half-cell elements, battery and control resistance for potentiometer circuit, double-pole double-throw switch, single-pole knife switch, key, one 50- and one 100-c.c. beaker, annunciator wire.

N/100 AgNO$_3$, N/10 AgNO$_3$, approx., N/5 AgNO$_3$, N/10 KCl, N KCl.

The wiring diagram for a " student " type of potentiometer is shown in Fig. 33, and the concentration cell assembly in Fig. 34.

The student type potentiometer is recommended for this exercise.

Method of Procedure:

Balance the potentiometer as follows: Set the slide wire dial B and the selector switch A for the value corresponding to the known E.M.F. of the standard cell.[1] Close S and throw X into the " standard cell " position. Quickly tap K, and note the deflection of the galvanometer. Adjust the regulating rheostat until no deflection of the galvanometer is noticed when K is closed. (*Note:* The key K should never be held down, as a current

[1] For the Weston cell the value of E at 20° C. is 1.0183, and at any other temperature t it is $E_t = E_{20} - 0.0000406\,(t - 20)$.

flow of any magnitude through the standard cell will cause its potential to rise or fall, through polarization.)

(a) *Determination of the degree of ionization of* $N/10$ $AgNO_3$.

In arranging the concentration cell, place the more concentrated solution in position L, normal KCl in the 50-c.c. beaker, and the more dilute solution in position R.

Since massive metals tend to give unreliable results, the silver electrodes should, prior to use, be given a thin coating of electro-deposited silver. This may be applied from a cyanide plating bath made up to contain 1.5 gm. $AgNO_3$ and 1.5 NaCN per 100 c.c. of solution. Several electrodes should be kept short-circuited in dilute $AgNO_3$ to preserve uniformity.

Set up the cell:

$$Ag : N/10 \; AgNO_3 : N \; KCl : N/100 \; AgNO_3 : Ag$$

and measure its potential.

(b) *Determination of ionic concentration in a silver solution of unknown concentration.*

Set up and measure the potential of the cell:

$$Ag : N/x \; AgNO_3 : N \; KCl : N/100 \; AgNO_3 : Ag$$

(c) *Determination of the solubility of silver chloride.*

Set up and measure the potential of the cell:

$$Ag : N/100 \; AgNO_3 : N \; KCl : N/10 \; KCl \; \text{saturated}$$
$$\text{with AgCl} : Ag$$

(The half-cell containing $N/10$ KCl saturated with AgCl is prepared by filling a cell with $N/10$ KCl, and adding to it a few drops of $N/5$ $AgNO_3$.)

Observations and Measurements:

(a) E.M.F. of the cell: $N/10 - N/100$ $AgNO_3$ ......
(b) E.M.F. of the cell: $N/x - N/100$ $AgNO_3$ ......
(c) E.M.F. of the cell: $N/100$ $AgNO_3$ − saturated AgCl....

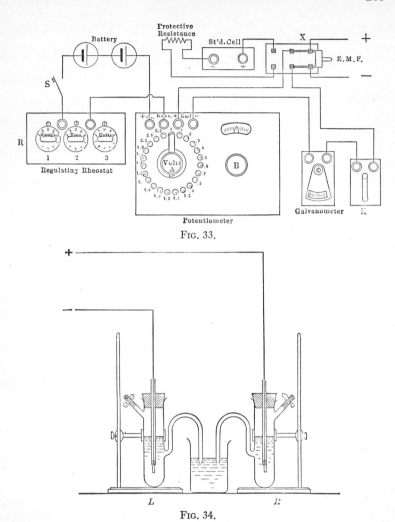

Fig. 33.

Fig. 34.

Calculations:

1. Knowing that the degree of dissociation of $N/100$ $AgNO_3$ is 0.93, calculate the degree of dissociation of $N/10$ $AgNO_3$.

2. Calculate the ionic concentration (αC) in the $AgNO_3$-solution of unknown concentration.

3. Assuming that a saturated solution of silver chloride is completely dissociated, calculate the solubility of silver chloride in mols per liter and the solubility product.

HYDROGEN ION CONCENTRATION: ELECTROMETRIC TITRATION

Object:

To measure hydrogen ion concentration electrometrically, to employ these measurements in the titration of acids and bases, and to observe the point of color change of some indicators.

Discussion:

It was shown in Experiment 38 that the single potential between a metal and a solution of one of its salts is a function of the concentration of the metallic ion. In the same way, the single potential between a " hydrogen electrode " and an aqueous solution is a function of the hydrogen ion concentration in that solution.

The hydrogen electrode consists of a small piece of platinum- or gold-foil, covered with platinum black and saturated with hydrogen gas. This is accomplished by surrounding the foil by a perforated glass mantel through which pure hydrogen is passed at a slow rate. The reaction at the electrode may be expressed by the equation:

$$H_2 \rightleftharpoons 2H^{\cdot} + 2\,(-)$$

In using the hydrogen electrode, one employs it together with a calomel electrode in a cell of the following type: calomel electrode (containing normal KCl) $\|$ solution investigated $\|$ hydrogen electrode for which the E.M.F. is given by the equation:

$$E.M.F. = 0.283 + 0.059\,pH$$

where: pH equals $-\log c_H$.

With this relationship between observed E.M.F. and hydrogen ion concentration available, it is evident that the hydrogen electrode may be used for measuring hydrolysis, for following the progress of neutralization reactions and for determining the pH values at which indicators change color.

Apparatus and Chemicals required:

Instead of the potentiometer with accessory equipment used in Experiment 38, the following simpler outfit may be substituted: Standard cell, normal KCl calomel electrode, hydrogen electrode,[1] slide wire potentiometer (resistance 3 ohms), battery (2 volts), adjustable resistance (about 10 ohms), single-pole single-throw switch, single-pole double-throw switch, portable galvanometer, key, sliding contact, Kipp hydrogen generator with wash bottles, motor and stirring device, clamps and iron stand, 2 burettes, 25-c.c. pipette, 150-c.c. beaker, graduated cylinder.

Stock bottles containing tenth-normal HCl, CH_3COOH, NaOH, and NH_4OH, N/5 Na_2CO_3, indicator solutions (methyl orange, phenolphthalein, cochineal).

The arrangement of the apparatus is shown in Fig. 35. The battery B supplying current to the potentiometer wire may consist of two dry cells, although it will be found much more satisfactory to use two Edison cells or one lead accumulator. In the circuit with the battery and the potentiometer wire MN are the switch S and the adjustable resistance E. The calomel electrode C and the positive side of the standard cell W are connected to the positive end M of the potentiometer wire. The negative side of the standard cell and the hydrogen electrode H are connected to the outside contacts of the double-throw switch D, while one terminal of the galvanometer G is attached to the central terminal of the switch D. The other end of the galvanometer is connected through the key K to the sliding contact P.

The iron stand with clamps carrying the motor, stirring device, calomel electrode, hydrogen electrode and burettes is not shown. The Kipp generator (or preferably the hydrogen tank) and the wash bottles are also left out. In case a generator is used, arsenic-free zinc and acid should be employed.

[1] The quinhydrone electrode is satisfactory for values of pH greater than 8. It consists of a Pt or Au wire dipping in N/200 quinhydrone solution. This electrode dispenses with the stream of hydrogen gas.

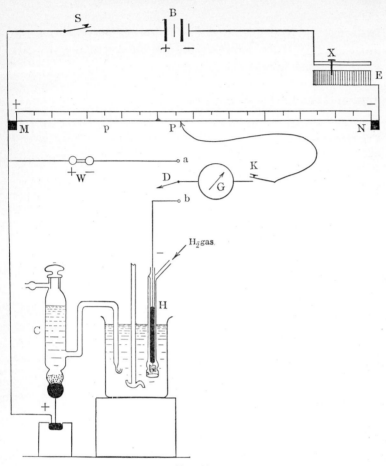

FIG. 35.

Method of Procedure:

In carrying out electromotive force measurements with a potentiometer it is necessary first to establish a known drop of potential across the calibrated portion of the wire. The E.M.F. of the standard cadmium cell is 1.0186 volt at 20° (temperature coefficient between 15 and 25° equals −0.0004 per degree). If, therefore, the sliding contact be set at 50.93 cm. (for a room temperature of 20°) and the current in the potentiometer circuit so regulated that the drop in potential along the wire between M and P is equal to the potential of the standard cell, then each centimeter on the potentiometer scale from M to any point p will correspond to a potential of 0.02 volt.

In order to regulate the current in the potentiometer circuit, throw switch D into position a, thereby making connection with the standard cell.   Close S and set P at the proper reading (50.93), then close key K for an *instant* by a *light tap* and note which way the galvanometer needle is deflected.   Do not allow an appreciable current to flow through the standard cell or its E.M.F. will be altered.   Shift contact point X and again close the galvanometer key K.   A few observations of this character will suffice to adjust X until no deflection is noted when K is closed.   When this is the case, the drop along MP is equal to the E.M.F. of the standard cell.

Having properly adjusted the current of the potentiometer circuit, proceed with the measurement of the electromotive force set up when the side arm of the calomel electrode and the hydrogen electrode are immersed in a solution containing hydrogen ions.

A. Titration of NaOH with HCl.

Slip the wooden block from beneath the titration beaker, empty the latter and rinse with distilled water, taking care to rinse the electrodes and stirring device also.

Replace the beaker, add 25 c.c. of distilled water, pipette 25 c.c. of tenth normal NaOH into it and add two drops of methyl orange.   In rinsing the beaker and the electrodes, work rapidly, in order that the hydrogen electrode may not be exposed to the air longer than is absolutely necessary.   Fill one burette with tenth normal HCl.

Start the stirring device and pass a brisk stream of hydrogen through the electrode.

Throw switch D into position b, thereby connecting the hydrogen electrode with the sliding contact P.   Depress K for an instant and adjust the position of P until no deflection is noted on the galvanometer when the key is closed.   Avoid passing a large current through the " gas chain " or it will become polarized.

Record the position of P, taking consecutive half-minute readings until a constant value is obtained.

Add 5 c.c. of HCl from the burette and obtain a new value. Continue the addition of acid, measuring potentials after adding 10, 15, 18, 21, 22.5, 23, 23.6, 24, 24.2, 24.3, ..., ... 26.4, 26.5, 27, 27.5, 28, 29 and 30 c.c. Make note of first and second color change of the indicator.

B. Titration of NH₄OH with HCl.

Check the adjustment of the potentiometer current by throwing the switch D into position a, setting the movable contact at 50.93 and if necessary readjusting the position of the contact X as previously directed.

After rinsing the titration vessel, electrodes and stirrer, place 25 c.c. of distilled water and 25 c.c., accurately measured, of tenth normal ammonia solution in the beaker. Add two drops of cochineal indicator.

Proceed as under A, recording simultaneously volumes of acid added, and potentiometer readings. Note the exact point at which the indicator changes.

C. Titration of Acetic Acid with NaOH.

Check the potentiometer current, replace the solution in the beaker with 25 c.c. of distilled water and 25 c.c. of acetic acid.

After adding two drops of phenolphthalein add, in this case from the second burette, tenth normal NaOH.

Record volumes and potentiometer readings as before and note the volume when the first permanent faint pink appears in the beaker.

D. Titration of Sodium Carbonate with HCl.

Place $N/5$ sodium carbonate solution (25 c.c.) in the cell, together with distilled water and a few drops of phenolphthalein.

Titrate with $N/10$ HCl until the solution is decolorized, then add methyl orange and titrate to acidity. Note the points at which the indicators change color and record the volumes and potentiometer readings.

Observations and Measurements:

A				B			
NaOH + HCl				NH$_4$OH + HCl			
Methyl orange				Cochineal			
c.c.	pot.	E.M.F.	pH	c.c.	pot.	E.M.F.	pH
....	....	....	....	....	....	....	....
....	....	....	....	....	....	....	....
....	....	....	....	....	....	....	....
....	....	....	....	....	....	....	....
....	....	....	....	....	....	....	....
....	....	....	....	....	....	....	....
....	....	....	....	....	....	....	....
....	....	....	....	....	....	....	....
....	....	....	....	....	....	....	....
....	....	....	....	....	....	....	....
....	....	....	....	....	....	....	....
....	....	....	....	....	....	....	....
....	....	....	....	....	....	....	....
....	....	....	....	....	....	....	....
....	....	....	....	....	....	....	....
....	....	....	....	....	....	....	....
....	....	....	....	....	....	....	....
....	....	....	....	....	....	....	....
....	....	....	....	....	....	....	....
....	....	....	....	....	....	....	....
....	....	....	....	....	....	....	....
....	....	....	....	....	....	....	....
....	....	....	....	....	....	....	....
....	....	....	....	....	....	....	....
....	....	....	....	....	....	....	....
....	....	....	....	....	....	....	....
....	....	....	....	....	....	....	....
....	....	....	....	....	....	....	....
....	....	....	....	....	....	....	....
....	....	....	....	....	....	....	....
....	....	....	....	....	....	....	....
....	....	....	....	....	....	....	....
....	....	....	....	....	....	....	....
....	....	....	....	....	....	....	....
....	....	....	....	....	....	....	....
....	....	....	....	....	....	....	....
....	....	....	....	....	....	....	....
....	....	....	....	....	....	....	....

c.c.	C CH$_3$COOH + HCl Phenolphthalein pot.	E.M.F.	pH	c.c.	D Na$_2$CO$_3$ + HCl Phenolphthalein, Methyl orange pot.	E.M.F.	pH
....	....	....	....	....	....	....	....
....	....	....	....	....	....	....	....
....	....	....	....	....	....	....	....
....	....	....	....	....	....	....	....
....	....	....	....	....	....	....	....
....	....	....	....	....	....	....	....
....	....	....	....	....	....	....	....
....	....	....	....	....	....	....	....
....	....	....	....	....	....	....	....
....	....	....	....	....	....	....	....
....	....	....	....	....	....	....	....
....	....	....	....	....	....	....	....
....	....	....	....	....	....	....	....
....	....	....	....	....	....	....	....
....	....	....	....	....	....	....	....
....	....	....	....	....	....	....	....
....	....	....	....	....	....	....	....
....	....	....	....	....	....	....	....
....	....	....	....	....	....	....	....
....	....	....	....	....	....	....	....
....	....	....	....	....	....	....	....
....	....	....	....	....	....	....	....
....	....	....	....	....	....	....	....
....	....	....	....	....	....	....	....
....	....	....	....	....	....	....	....
....	....	....	....	....	....	....	....
....	....	....	....	....	....	....	....
....	....	....	....	....	....	....	....
....	....	....	....	....	....	....	....
....	....	....	....	....	....	....	....
....	....	....	....	....	....	....	....
....	....	....	....	....	....	....	....
....	....	....	....	....	....	....	....
....	....	....	....	....	....	....	....
....	....	....	....	....	....	....	....
....	....	....	....	....	....	....	....
....	....	....	....	....	....	....	....

Calculations:

1. Multiply the potentiometer readings by 0.02 in order to obtain the E.M.F.

2. Calculate the value of pH in each case from the equation for the cell: |calomel electrode (containing normal KCl) ‖ solution ‖ hydrogen electrode]

$$E.M.F. = 0.283 + 0.0591 \, pH$$

or, approximate the value of pH from the pH-E.M.F. curve (Fig. 36).

3. Plot the number of c.c. of reagent added against pH for each titration made, noting the neutral point ($pH = 7$) and also the point at which the indicator changed color.

4. If the latter did not change at the "neutral point" explain the discrepancy.

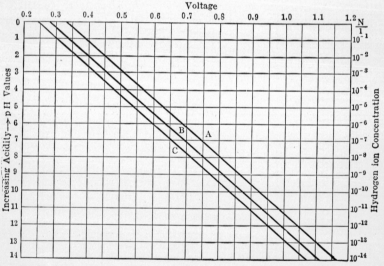

Graphs showing relation between voltage of gas chain and hydrogen ion concentration (pH).
  A. for a 0.1 Normal KCl calomel electrode.
  B. for a Normal calomel electrode.
  C. for a saturated KCl calomel electrode.

FIG. 36.

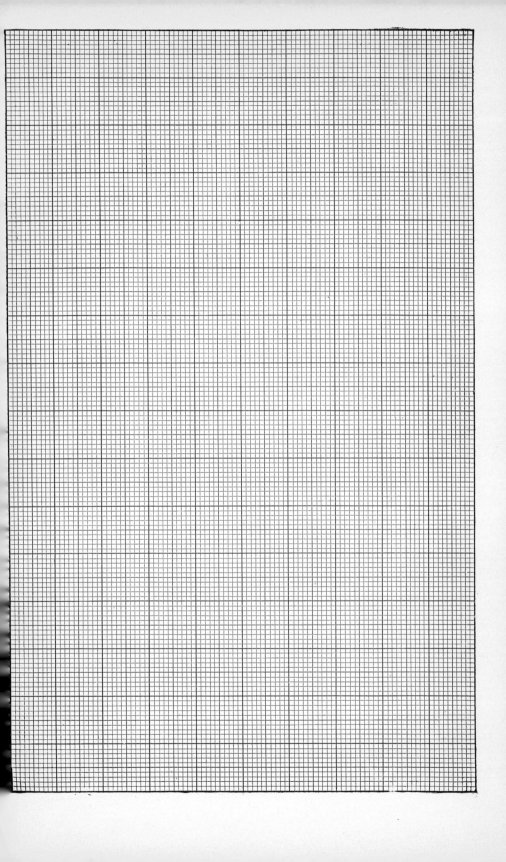

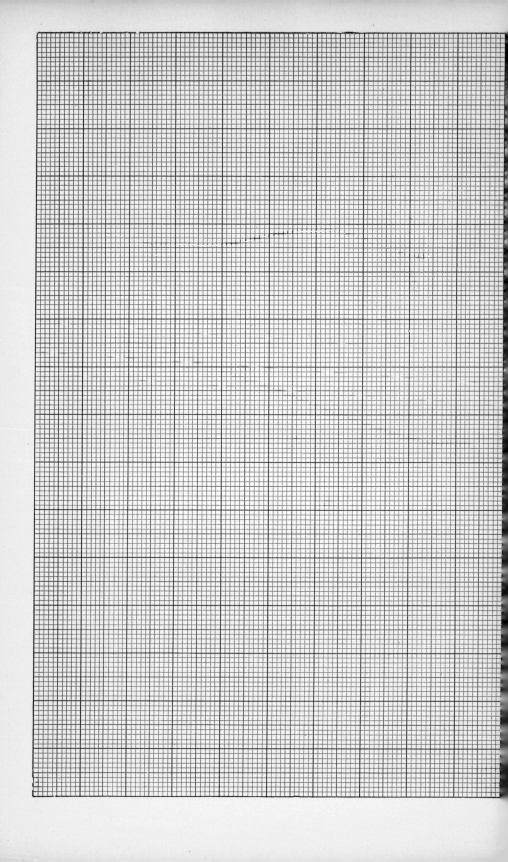

EXPERIMENT 40

INDICATORS, BUFFER SOLUTIONS, HYDROLYSIS

Object:

To determine the constant for an indicator; to prepare buffer solutions of known pH value; to measure unknown hydrogen ion concentrations by means of indicators; and to determine the degrees of hydrolysis of various salts.

Discussion:

Indicator Constant (K_I):

If one designates by x the fraction of the total quantity of an indicator present in a given equilibrium which has been transformed to the " alkaline " color, and by $1 - x$ the fraction remaining in the " acid " color:

$$K_I = (H^+) \frac{x}{1 - x}$$

For the indicator phenolphthalein, the constant may be determined experimentally by the following method: A series of color standards is prepared, each containing a known quantity of indicator. The indicator in each standard is totally transferred to the red modification by an excess of alkali. A buffer solution, containing a known amount of indicator, is prepared to give some definite pH value, at which the indicator is only partially transferred to the colored modification. The depth of this color is matched against the color standards, and the amount of phenolphthalein which has been transformed to the pink form is estimated. Substitution in the equation given above enables one to calculate the indicator constant.

Buffer Solutions:

While it is theoretically possible to prepare a solution of any desired pH value by dissolving the proper amount of acid or base in water, practically it is impossible to maintain such a solution on account of the changes wrought by dissolved gases, and by the small amount of alkali leached from the glass container.

The usual method of preparing such solutions utilizes buffer salts. The solutions are made up to a greater total acidity or alkalinity than is desired, and ionization of the acid or base is driven back to the desired pH value by the introduction of some compound, usually a salt furnishing a common ion. If one neglects the slight dissociation of buffered weak acids or bases, he may write the following expressions:

For a weak acid, buffered by one of its salts:

$$(\text{H}^+) = \frac{(HA)}{(A^-)} \times K_{HA}$$

where: (HA) is the concentration of the acid,

(A^-) the concentrations of anion resulting from dissociation of the salt,

and K_{HA} the ionization product of the acid.

For a weak base buffered by one of its salts:

$$(\text{OH}^-) = \frac{1 \times 10^{-14}}{(H^+)} = \frac{(BOH)}{(C^+)} \times K_{BOH}$$

where (C^+) is the concentration of the cation resulting from dissociation of the buffer salt.

Determination of Hydrogen Ion Concentrations by the use of Indicators:

Indicators do not change color abruptly at given values of pH, but rather undergo gradual changes in color and depth of color, between definite limits of hydrogen ion concentration. These limits vary with the different indicators. pH values lying between the useful limits for a given indicator are said to lie within the range for that indicator. Thus, phenolphthalein, which undergoes definite changes in shade between pH values of 8.3 and 10.0, is said to have a range of 8.3 − 10.0. It is evident that if one were to construct a color scale, by placing phenolphthalein in solutions of graded pH values lying between 8.3 and 10.0, he would be able to determine the pH of an unknown solution (if it is within the phenolphthalein range) by adding the same amount of indicator to it, and matching the color so obtained against the standard phenolphthalein color scale. The limit of accuracy for this method is about 0.2 pH.

The number of indicators available is very large, and their individual ranges run from as low as 0.1 to as high as 13.0. By careful selection, one may eliminate the majority of them, and still be able to cover the useful range for hydrogen ion work. Such a series (Clark, Lubs, Cohen) modified by the authors is:

Indicator	Range	Color	$-\log K_I$	Composition of solution,* per cent
1. Thymol blue.....	1.2– 2.8	red-yellow	1.5	0.04
2. Brom phenol blue.	3.0– 4.6	yellow-blue	3.98	0.04
3. Chlor phenol red.	4.8– 6.4	yellow-red	5.98	0.04
4. Brom thymol blue	6.0– 7.6	yellow-blue	7.0	0.04
5. Phenol red......	6.8– 8.4	yellow-red	7.9	0.02
or Cresol red...	7.2– 8.8	yellow-red	8.3	0.02
6. Phenolphthalein..	8.3–10.0	colorless-red	9.7	0.02
7. Alizarine yellow R	10.1–12.1	colorless-yellow	....	0.01

* Indicator stock solutions are usually made up by dissolving 0.1 gram of indicator in 50 cms. of 95 per cent alcohol. To make 0.04 per cent indicator solution, mix 10 c.c. of the above stock solution with 40 c.c. of water; to make 0.02 per cent indicator solution mix 5 c.c. of stock solution with 45 c.c. of water; and for 0.01 per cent take 2.5 c.c. stock solution and 47.5 c.c. water.

The Use of Indicators in Determining Degree of Hydrolysis:

In this experiment, two different methods for determining degree of hydrolysis are employed.

In the first method, we will determine the degree of hydrolysis and the hydrolysis constant for sodium borate, and the ionization product for boric acid, by adding sodium hydroxide to boric acid until the pH of the solution falls within the range for phenolphthalein, when it will be determined.   We will read the amounts of boric acid and of sodium hydroxide used.

When pH of the solution lies within the range for phenol-phthalein, there will still be an excess of boric acid present.   If we assume that the solution is sufficiently dilute for all the base added to have liberated borate ion, we find, denoting by a the number of equivalents of HBO_2 originally present, and by b the sodium hydroxide added, that

$$b/a = \frac{(BO_2^-)}{(HBO_3)}$$ (1)

The ionization equation for boric acid is:

$$K_{HA} = \frac{(H^+) \cdot (BO_2^-)}{(HBO_3)}$$ (2)

substituting (1) in (2) we obtain,

$$K_{HA} = (H^+) \cdot b/a$$ (3)

We can measure (H^+), a and b.

The hydrolysis constant K_H for the salt of a weak acid and strong base is:

$$K_H = \frac{K_{H_2O}}{K_{HA}} = \frac{\alpha_b}{\alpha_s} \cdot \frac{x^2}{(1-x)V}$$ (4)

where: K_{H_2O} is the ionization product for water,
   α_b and α_s the degrees of dissociation for base and salt, respectively (assume these to be equal to unity)
   x the degree of hydrolysis;
and V the volume in liters required to contain one equivalent of salt.

The second method for determining the degree of hydrolysis by the use of indicators merely involves the determination of the hydrogen ion concentration in a solution of known concentration of the salt under investigation.   The equation for the hydrolysis constant has been given above (4).

If the salt produces a strong acid and a weak base by hydrolysis, the hydrogen ion concentration and the concentration of the acid anion, and the concentration of the weak base are all x/V. Measurement of the hydrogen ion concentration, therefore, enables one to calculate x, since V is known.

If the salt produces a strong base and a weak acid on hydrolysis, we have:

$$C_{OH^-} = \frac{1 \times 10^{-14}}{C_{H^+}}$$

Apparatus required:

Variable depth colorimeter (or six Nessler tubes, or even six uniform 6 by 1 inch test tubes), eight 100-c.c. volumetric flasks, two burettes, one 5-c.c. Mohr pipette, one 10-c.c., one 25-c.c., and one 50-c.c. pipette, twelve test tubes, test-tube rack.

Saturated aqueous phenolphthalein solution, solutions of seven indicators listed on page 219, N/10 NH₄Cl, N/10 NH₄OH, 10 per cent NaOH, N/10 HBO₂, N/10 NaOH, aniline hydrochloride, ammonium chloride, sodium carbonate, potassium cyanide, sodium acetate.

Buffers: It is recommended that the six stock solutions listed in Table 17 of the Appendix be available, so that students can make their own specific buffer solutions.

Method of Procedure:

A. *Indicator Constant:*

Prepare a fresh series of color standards, labeled 1 to 5, by placing exactly 1, 2, 3, 4, and 5 c.c. of saturated phenolphthalein solution in 100-c.c. volumetric flasks, adding to each about 75 c.c. of distilled water + 0.5 c.c. of 10 per cent NaOH, and filling the flasks to the mark with water. (*Note:* If a variable depth colorimeter is available, it will only be necessary to prepare standard No. 5.)

Prepare a buffer solution, containing 50 c.c. N/10 NH₄Cl, 10 c.c N/10 NH₄OH, and 40 c.c. of phenolphthalein solution. Compare its depth of color with the standards, using either a colorimeter, Nessler tubes, or even uniform test tubes. If a colorimeter is not available, estimate shades lying between two adjacent tubes as accurately as possible, being careful to make all observations through the same depth of liquid.

Record the data under " Observations and Measurements."

B. *Hydrolysis of Sodium Borate* (*First Method*):

Place 25 c.c. of N/10 boric acid in a 100-c.c. volumetric flask, add 40 c.c. of indicator solution, and titrate with N/10 NaOH until the pink color of the indicator falls within the range of the color scale established under A. Fill the flask to the mark, place some of the solution in a comparison tube, compare the shade obtained with the color standards, and record the result. Also record the volume of NaOH used in the titration.

C. *Measurement of Unknown Hydrogen Ion Concentrations:*

Before one can accurately determine the pH of an unknown solution by means of indicators, it is necessary to ascertain which indicator includes the unknown pH within its range. To do this, place about 5 c.c. of the solution in a small test-tube, add three drops of indicator No. 4, and note whether the indicator assumes its " acid " or its " alkaline " color. If " alkaline," proceed to test, in turn, Nos. 5, 6, and 7, until the proper one is found. If acid, go down the indicator scale.

When you have determined which indicator is the correct one to use, secure the buffer solutions corresponding to its range. In some laboratories, buffer solutions are supplied by the instructor; in others, students prepare their own. Consult Table 17, Appendix, for data on buffer solutions. Place 10 c.c. of each buffer solution required in small labeled test tubes, and add 0.5 c.c. of indicator solution to each tube.

Place 10 c.c. of the unknown solution in a similar tube, and add 0.5 c.c. of indicator to it. Determine the pH value of the solution by matching the color so obtained against the buffer-indicator colors. Record the pH.

D. *Determination of Hydrolysis* (*Second Method*):

Prepare a dilute solution (say M/100) of the salt assigned for study, and measure its pH as in C. Record the results.

Observations and Measurements:

A. Indicator Constant.
   Color standard matched by $NH_4OH - NH_4Cl$ solution: ....
   c.c phenolphthalein in red modification: ....
   Total volume phenolphthalein present: ....
   Per cent transformed to pink modification:........
   H-ion concentration (calculated):   ....
   K_1.
B. Hydrolysis of Sodium Borate.
   Volume boric acid used: ....
   Volume sodium hydroxide used: ....
   Color standard matched: ....
   c.c phenolphthalein in red modification: ....
   Volume phenolphthalein present: ....
   Per cent transformed: ....
   H-ion concentration (determined):   ....
   Ionization constant K_{HA} for HBO_2:   ....
   Hydrolysis constant K_H for $NaBO_2$:   ....
   Per cent hydrolysis, x: ....
C. Determination of pH. Solution marked:..Indicator used:..
   Range:...... pH found:...... H^+ conc.:........
D. Hydrolysis, second method. Salt used: ....
                                 Concentration:........
   Indicator: ....   Range: ....
   pH found: .... H^+ conc.:   ....
                             OH^- conc.:   ....
   Degree of hydrolysis, x: ....
   K_H found: ....
   K_{HA} or K_{BOH}:   ....

Calculations:

1. Calculate the hydrogen ion concentration for the $NH_4OH - NH_4Cl$ buffer solution, and determine the indicator constant for phenolphthalein.

2. From the $HBO_2 - NaOH$ titration, determine the H-ion concentration, and calculate the ionization constant for boric

acid; the hydrolysis constant, and the degree of hydrolysis of sodium borate.

3. Calculate the degree of hydrolysis, and the hydrolysis constant for the salt in D. Also calculate the ionization constant for the weak acid or weak base involved.

TABLES

TABLE 1

VAPOR PRESSURE OF WATER IN MM. MERCURY

At Low Temperatures

4°	6.1	19°	16.5
5	6.5	20	17.5
6	7.0	21	18.7
7	7.5	22	19.8
8	8.0	23	21.1
9	8.6	24	22.4
10	9.2	25	23.8
11	9.8	26	25.2
12	10.5	27	26.7
13	11.2	28	28.4
14	12.0	29	30.1
15	12.8	30	31.8
16	13.6	31	33.7
17	14.5	32	35.7
18	15.5	33	37.7

TABLE 2

VAPOR PRESSURE OF WATER IN MM. MERCURY

At High Temperatures

Boiling Point	Pressure	Boiling Point	Pressure
90	526.0	97	682.1
	20.3		25.2
91	546.3	98	707.3
	20.9		26.0
92	567.2	99	733.3
	21.6		26.7
93	588.8	100	760.0
	22.2		27.6
94	611.0	101	787.6
	23.0		28.4
95	634.0	102	816.0
	23.7		29.3
96	657.7	103	845.3
	24.4		30.1
97	682.1	104	875.4

TABLE 3

REFRACTIVE INDEX OF WATER FOR SODIUM LIGHT AT DIFFERENT TEMPERATURES

Temperature ° C.	Refractive Index	Temperature ° C.	Refractive Index
0	1.33395	22	1.33283
5	1.33388	23	1.33274
10	1.33368	24	1.33264
15	1.33337	25	1.33254
16	1.33330	26	1.33243
.17	1.33323	27	1.33231
18	1.33316	28	1.33219
19	1.33308	29	1.33206
20	1.33300	30	1.33192
21	1.33292		

TABLE 4

DENSITIES (d_4) OF VARIOUS LIQUIDS

A. MERCURY (Régnault-Broch)

0°	13.5956	8	13.5759	15	13.5586	40	13.4974
1	13.5931	9	13.5734	16	13.5562	50	13.4731
2	13.5907	10	13.5709	17	13.5537	60	13.4488
3	13.5882	11	13.5685	18	13.5513	70	13.4246
4	13.5857	12	13.5660	19	13.5488	80	13.4005
5	13.5833	13	13.5635	20	13.5463	90	13.3764
6	13.5808	14	13.5611	30	13.5218	100	13.3524
7	13.5783						

B. WATER (Thiesen, Scheel, Marek)

0°	0.9999	5	1.0000	10	0.9997	60	0.9833
1	0.9999	6	1.0000	20	0.9982	70	0.9779
2	1.0000	7	0.9999	30	0.9957	80	0.9719
3	1.0000	8	0.9999	40	0.9923	90	0.9655
4	1.0000*	9	0.9998	50	0.9881	B.P.100	0.9586

C. NITROBENZENE (van Klooster)

0°	1.224	30	1.194	60	1.164	90	1.133
10	1.214	40	1.184	70	1.154	100	1.123
20	1.204	50	1.174	80	1.143		

D. CHLOROBENZENE (Jaeger)

0°	1.128	30	1.095	60	1.062	90	1.029
10	1.117	40	1.084	70	1.051	100	1.018
20	1.106	50	1.073	80	1.040		

E. Bromobenzene (Jaeger)

0°	1.520	30	1.480[5]	60	1.440	90	1.400
10	1.507	40	1.467	70	1.427	100	1.387
20	1.494	50	1.453[5]	80	1.413[5]		

F. Carbon tetrachloride (Jaeger)

0°	1.632	30	1.576	50	1.536	70	1.494
10	1.615	40	1.555	60	1.516	B.P. 76	1.480
20	1.597						

TABLE 5

FREEZING-POINT CONSTANTS (per 100 Grams of Solvent)

Substance	Freezing Point at 760 mm.	Freezing-point Constant K_F
Water...................	0°	18.6°
Acetic acid...............	17	39
Benzene................	5.5	51.2
Naphthalene.............	80.1	69
Phenol..................	38	70

TABLE 6

BOILING-POINT CONSTANTS (per 100 Grams of Solvent) [1]

Substance	Boiling Point at 760 mm.	Boiling-point Constant K_B
Water...................	100°	5.2°
Acetic acid...............	118.5	32.8
Benzene................	80.15	25.8
Carbon tetrachloride...........	76.5	50.5
Chloroform...............	60.2	36.4
Ether...................	34.4	22.1
Ethyl acetate.............	77.1	29.0

[1] From Rosanoff and Dunphy, J. Am. Chem. Soc., *36*, 1415 (1914).

TABLE 7

DENSITY, PERCENTAGE (Grams of HCl per 100 Grams of Solution) and NORMALITY
of Aqueous Solutions of HYDROCHLORIC ACID

d_4^{15}	% HCl	Normality	d_4^{15}	% HCl	Normality
1.000	0.16	0.044	1.100	20.01	6.035
1.005	1.15	0.317	1.105	20.97	6.354
1.010	2.14	0.593	1.110	21.92	6.671
1.015	3.12	0.868	1.115	22.86	6.989
1.020	4.13	1.155	1.120	23.82	7.315
1.025	5.15	1.447	1.125	24.78	7.644
1.030	6.15	1.737	1.130	25.75	7.978
1.035	7.15	2.029	1.135	26.70	8.309
1.040	8.16	2.327	1.140	27.66	8.646
1.045	9.16	2.625	1.145	28.61	8.982
1.050	10.17	2.928	1.150	29.57	9.324
1.055	11.18	3.234	1.155	30.55	9.675
1.060	12.19	3.543	1.160	31.52	10.03
1.065	13.19	3.852	1.165	32.49	10.38
1.070	14.17	4.157	1.170	33.46	10.73
1.075	15.16	4.470	1.175	34.42	11.09
1.080	16.15	4.782	1.180	35.39	11.45
1.085	17.13	5.096	1.185	36.31	11.80
1.090	18.11	5.413	1.190	37.23	12.15
1.095	19.06	5.723	1.195	38.16	12.50
1.100	20.01	6.035	1.200	39.11	12.87

TABLE 8

DENSITY AND SPECIFIC HEAT OF DIFFERENT SUBSTANCES AT ROOM TEMPERATURE

Substance	Density	Specific Heat
Glass..........................	2.5	0.19
Mercury......................	13.5	0.034
Brass.........................	8.5	0.094
Copper.......................	8.8	0.092
Gold..........................	19.3	0.0315
Iron..........................	7.85	0.115
Nickel........................	9.1	0.109
Platinum......................	20.3	0.032
Steel.........................	....	0.116
Silver	10.53	0.055

TABLE 9

SPECIFIC CONDUCTANCE OF FIFTIETH-NORMAL KCl

(containing 1.492 Grams per Liter) at
Different Temperatures

Temperature	Conductance	Temperature	Conductance
10°	0.001521	24°	0.002712
15	0.002243	25	0.002765
18	0.002397	26	0.002819
20	0.002501	30	0.003036

TABLE 10

EQUIVALENT CONDUCTANCES AT INFINITE DILUTION OF WEAK ACIDS at 25°

Acetic acid....................389   Oxalic acid....................422.7
Benzoic acid...................381   Succinic acid..................381
Cinnamic acid.................378.5

TABLE 11

TRANSPORT NUMBERS OF CATIONS AT 18°

	N/100	N/10	N/1
$AgNO_3$	.471	.471	.465
KNO_3	——	.502	——
KCl	.496	.495	——
HNO_3	——	.855	——
HCl	.833	.835	——
$CuSO_4$	.375	.373	.330
H_2SO_4	.824	.824	——

MAXIMUM IONIC CONDUCTANCES AT 18°

Na^+	43.5	Cu^{++}	46.0
Ag^+	54.3	Cl^-	65.5
K^+	64.6	NO_2^-	61.7
H^+	315.0	SO_4^{--}	68.0

TABLE 12

REDUCTION OF BAROMETER READINGS TO 0°

When the height of the mercury column has been measured with a glass or a brass scale, the length of which is correct at o°, the mercury and the scale being at $t°$, the observed height is reduced to o° by *subtracting* the value given in the table corresponding to the temperature and height.

	GLASS SCALE (Bunsen)						BRASS SCALE (Delcros)				
Temperature.	Barometer Reading in mm.					Temperature.	Barometer Reading in mm.				
	740	750	760	770	780		740	750	760	770	780
1°	0.13	0.13	0.13	0.13	0.14	1°	0.12	0.12	0.12	0.13	0.13
2	0.26	0.26	0.26	0.27	0.27	2	0.24	0.25	0.25	0.25	0.25
3	0.38	0.39	0.39	0.40	0.41	3	0.36	0.37	0.37	0.38	0.38
4	0.51	0.52	0.53	0.53	0.54	4	0.48	0.49	0.50	0.50	0.51
5	0.64	0.65	0.66	0.67	0.68	5	0.60	0.61	0.62	0.63	0.64
6	0.77	0.78	0.79	0.80	0.81	6	0.72	0.73	0.74	0.75	0.76
7	0.90	0.91	0.92	0.93	0.95	7	0.85	0.86	0.87	0.88	0.89
8	1.02	1.04	1.05	1.07	1.08	8	0.97	0.98	0.99	1.01	1.02
9	1.15	1.17	1.18	1.20	1.21	9	1.09	1.10	1.12	1.13	1.15
10	1.28	1.30	1.31	1.33	1.35	10	1.21	1.22	1.24	1.26	1.27
11	1.41	1.43	1.45	1.46	1.48	11	1.33	1.35	1.36	1.38	1.40
12	1.53	1.56	1.58	1.60	1.62	12	1.45	1.47	1.49	1.51	1.53
13	1.66.	1.69	1.71	1.73	1.75	13	1.57	1.59	1.61	1.63	1.65
14	1.79	1.81	1.84	1.86	1.89	14	1.69	1.71	1.73	1.76	1.78
15	1.92	1.94	1.97	2.00	2.02	15	1.81	1.83	1.86	1.88	1.91
16	2.05	2.07	2.10	2.13	2.16	16	1.93	1.96	1.98	2.01	2.03
17	2.17	2.20	2.23	2.26	2.29	17	2.05	2.08	2.10	2.13	2.16
18	2.30	2.33	2.36	2.39	2.43	18	2.17	2.20	2.23	2.26	2.29
19	2.43	2.46	2.49	2.53	2.56	19	2.29	2.32	2.35	2.38	2.41
20	2.56	2.59	2.62	2.66	2.69	20	2.41	2.44	2.47	2.51	2.54
21	2.08	2.72	2.76	2.79	2.83	21	2.53	2.56	2.60	2.63	2.67
22	2.81	2.85	2.89	2.92	2.96	22	2.65	2.69	2.72	2.76	2.79
23	2.94	2.98	3.02	3.06	3.10	23	2.77	2.81	2.84	2.88	2.92
24	3.06	3.11	3.15	3.19	3.23	24	2.89	2.93	2.97	3.01	3.05
25	3.19	3.23	3.28	3.32	3.36	25	3.01	3.05	3.09	3.13	3.17
26	3.32	3.36	3.41	3.45	3.50	26	3.13	3.17	3.21	3.26	3.30
27	3.45	3.49	3.54	3.59	3.63	27	3.25	3.29	3.34	3.38	3.42
28	3.57	3.62	3.67	3.72	3.77	28	3.37	3.41	3.46	3.51	3.55
29	3.70	3.75	3.80	3.85	3.90	29	3.49	3.54	3.58	3.63	3.68
30	3.83	3.88	3.93	3.98	4.03	30	3.61	3.66	3.71	3.75	3.80

TABLE 13

Four Place Logarithms

	0	1	2	3	4	5	6	7	8	9	1	2	3	4	5	6	7	8	9
											Proportionality factors								
10	0000	0043	0086	0128	0170	0212	0253	0294	0334	0374	4	8	12	17	21	25	29	33	37
11	0414	0453	0492	0531	0569	0607	0645	0682	0719	0755	4	8	11	15	19	23	26	30	34
12	0792	0828	0864	0899	0934	0969	1004	1038	1072	1106	3	7	10	14	17	21	24	28	31
13	1139	1173	1206	1239	1271	1303	1335	1367	1399	1430	3	6	10	13	16	19	23	26	29
14	1461	1492	1523	1553	1584	1614	1644	1673	1703	1732	3	6	9	12	15	18	21	24	27
15	1761	1790	1818	1847	1875	1903	1931	1959	1987	2014	3	6	8	11	14	17	20	22	25
16	2041	2068	2095	2122	2148	2175	2201	2227	2253	2279	3	5	8	11	13	16	18	21	24
17	2304	2330	2355	2380	2405	2430	2455	2480	2504	2529	2	5	7	10	12	15	17	20	22
18	2553	2577	2601	2625	2648	2672	2695	2718	2742	2765	2	5	7	9	12	14	16	19	21
19	2788	2810	2833	2856	2878	2900	2923	2945	2967	2989	2	4	7	9	11	13	16	18	20
20	3010	3032	3054	3075	3096	3118	3139	3160	3181	3201	2	4	6	8	11	13	15	17	19
21	3222	3243	3263	3284	3304	3324	3345	3365	3385	3404	2	4	6	8	10	12	14	16	18
22	3424	3444	3464	3483	3502	3522	3541	3560	3579	3598	2	4	6	8	10	12	14	15	17
23	3617	3636	3655	3674	3692	3711	3729	3747	3766	3784	2	4	6	7	9	11	13	15	17
24	3802	3820	3838	3856	3874	3892	3909	3927	3945	3962	2	4	5	7	9	11	12	14	16
25	3979	3997	4014	4031	4048	4065	4082	4099	4116	4133	2	3	5	7	9	10	12	14	15
26	4150	4166	4183	4200	4216	4232	4249	4265	4281	4298	2	3	5	7	8	10	11	13	15
27	4314	4330	4346	4362	4378	4393	4409	4425	4440	4456	2	3	5	6	8	9	11	13	14
28	4472	4487	4502	4518	4533	4548	4564	4579	4594	4609	2	3	5	6	8	9	11	12	14
29	4624	4639	4654	4669	4683	4698	4713	4728	4742	4757	1	3	4	6	7	9	10	12	13
30	4771	4786	4800	4814	4829	4843	4857	4871	4886	4900	1	3	4	6	7	9	10	11	13
31	4914	4928	4942	4955	4969	4983	4997	5011	5024	5038	1	3	4	6	7	8	10	11	12
32	5051	5065	5079	5092	5105	5119	5132	5145	5159	5172	1	3	4	5	7	8	9	11	12
33	5185	5198	5211	5224	5237	5250	5263	5276	5289	5302	1	3	4	5	6	8	9	10	12
34	5315	5328	5340	5353	5366	5378	5391	5403	5416	5428	1	3	4	5	6	8	9	10	11
35	5441	5453	5465	5478	5490	5502	5514	5527	5539	5551	1	2	4	5	6	7	9	10	11
36	5563	5575	5587	5599	5611	5623	5635	5647	5658	5670	1	2	4	5	6	7	8	10	11
37	5682	5694	5705	5717	5729	5740	5752	5763	5775	5786	1	2	3	5	6	7	8	9	10
38	5798	5809	5821	5832	5843	5855	5866	5877	5888	5899	1	2	3	5	6	7	8	9	10
39	5911	5922	5933	5944	5955	5966	5977	5988	5999	6010	1	2	3	4	5	7	8	9	10
40	6021	6031	6042	6053	6064	6075	6085	6096	6107	6117	1	2	3	4	5	6	8	9	10
41	6128	6138	6149	6160	6170	6180	6191	6201	6212	6222	1	2	3	4	5	6	7	8	9
42	6232	6243	6253	6263	6274	6284	6294	6304	6314	6325	1	2	3	4	5	6	7	8	9
43	6335	6345	6355	6365	6375	6385	6395	6405	6415	6425	1	2	3	4	5	6	7	8	9
44	6435	6444	6454	6464	6474	6484	6493	6503	6513	6522	1	2	3	4	5	6	7	8	9
45	6532	6542	6551	6561	6571	6580	6590	6599	6609	6618	1	2	3	4	5	6	7	8	9
46	6628	6637	6646	6656	6665	6675	6684	6693	6702	6712	1	2	3	4	5	6	7	7	8
47	6721	6730	6739	6749	6758	6767	6776	6785	6794	6803	1	2	3	4	5	5	6	7	8
48	6812	6821	6830	6839	6848	6857	6866	6875	6884	6893	1	2	3	4	4	5	6	7	8
49	6902	6911	6920	6928	6937	6946	6955	6964	6972	6981	1	2	3	4	4	5	6	7	8
50	6990	6998	7007	7016	7024	7033	7042	7050	7059	7067	1	2	3	3	4	5	6	7	8
51	7076	7084	7093	7101	7110	7118	7126	7135	7143	7152	1	2	3	3	4	5	6	7	8
52	7160	7168	7177	7185	7193	7202	7210	7218	7226	7235	1	2	2	3	4	5	6	7	7
53	7243	7251	7259	7267	7275	7284	7292	7300	7308	7316	1	2	2	3	4	5	6	6	7
54	7324	7332	7340	7348	7356	7364	7372	7380	7388	7396	1	2	2	3	4	5	6	6	7

TABLE 13.—FOUR PLACE LOGARITHMS (*Continued*)

	0	1	2	3	4	5	6	7	8	9	1	2	3	4	5	6	7	8	9
											Proportionality factors								
55	7404	7412	7419	7427	7435	7443	7451	7459	7466	7474	1	2	2	3	4	5	5	6	7
56	7482	7490	7497	7505	7513	7520	7528	7536	7543	7551	1	2	2	3	4	5	5	6	7
57	7559	7566	7574	7582	7589	7597	7604	7612	7619	7627	1	2	2	3	4	5	5	6	7
58	7634	7642	7649	7657	7664	7672	7679	7686	7694	7701	1	1	2	3	4	4	5	6	7
59	7709	7716	7723	7731	7738	7745	7752	7760	7767	7774	1	1	2	3	4	4	5	6	7
60	7782	7789	7796	7803	7810	7818	7825	7832	7839	7846	1	1	2	3	4	4	5	6	6
61	7853	7860	7868	7875	7882	7889	7896	7903	7910	7917	1	1	2	3	4	4	5	6	6
62	7924	7931	7938	7945	7952	7959	7966	7973	7980	7987	1	1	2	3	3	4	5	6	6
63	7993	8000	8007	8014	8021	8028	8035	8041	8048	8055	1	1	2	3	3	4	5	5	6
64	8062	8069	8075	8082	8089	8096	8102	8109	8116	8122	1	1	2	3	3	4	5	5	6
65	8129	8136	8142	8149	8156	8162	8169	8176	8182	8189	1	1	2	3	3	4	5	5	6
66	8195	8202	8209	8215	8222	8228	8235	8241	8248	8254	1	1	2	3	3	4	5	5	6
67	8261	8267	8274	8280	8287	8293	8299	8306	8312	8319	1	1	2	3	3	4	5	5	6
68	8325	8331	8338	8344	8351	8357	8363	8370	8376	8382	1	1	2	3	3	4	4	5	6
69	8388	8395	8401	8407	8414	8420	8426	8432	8439	8445	1	1	2	2	3	4	4	5	6
70	8451	8457	8463	8470	8476	8482	8488	8494	8500	8506	1	1	2	2	3	4	4	5	6
71	8513	8519	8525	8531	8537	8543	8549	8555	8561	8567	1	1	2	2	3	4	4	5	5
72	8573	8579	8585	8591	8597	8603	8609	8615	8621	8627	1	1	2	2	3	4	4	5	5
73	8633	8639	8645	8651	8657	8663	8669	8675	8681	8686	1	1	2	2	3	4	4	5	5
74	8692	8698	8704	8710	8716	8722	8727	8733	8739	8745	1	1	2	2	3	4	4	5	5
75	8751	8756	8762	8768	8774	8779	8785	8791	8797	8802	1	1	2	2	3	3	4	5	5
76	8808	8814	8820	8825	8831	8837	8842	8848	8854	8859	1	1	2	2	3	3	4	5	5
77	8865	8871	8876	8882	8887	8893	8899	8904	8910	8915	1	1	2	2	3	3	4	4	5
78	8921	8927	8932	8938	8943	8949	8954	8960	8965	8971	1	1	2	2	3	3	4	4	5
79	8976	8982	8987	8993	8998	9004	9009	9015	9020	9025	1	1	2	2	3	3	4	4	5
80	9031	9036	9042	9047	9053	9058	9063	9069	9074	9079	1	1	2	2	3	3	4	4	5
81	9085	9090	9096	9101	9106	9112	9117	9122	9128	9133	1	1	2	2	3	3	4	4	5
82	9138	9143	9149	9154	9159	9165	9170	9175	9180	9186	1	1	2	2	3	3	4	4	5
83	9191	9196	9201	9206	9212	9217	9222	9227	9232	9238	1	1	2	2	3	3	4	4	5
84	9243	9248	9253	9258	9263	9269	9274	9279	9284	9289	1	1	2	2	3	3	4	4	5
85	9294	9299	9304	9309	9315	9320	9325	9330	9335	9340	1	1	2	2	3	3	4	4	5
86	9345	9350	9355	9360	9365	9370	9375	9380	9385	9390	1	1	2	2	3	3	4	4	5
87	9395	9400	9405	9410	9415	9420	9425	9430	9435	9440	0	1	1	2	2	3	3	4	4
88	9445	9450	9455	9460	9465	9469	9474	9479	9484	9489	0	1	1	2	2	3	3	4	4
89	9494	9499	9504	9509	9513	9518	9523	9528	9533	9538	0	1	1	2	2	3	3	4	4
90	9542	9547	9552	9557	9562	9566	9571	9576	9581	9586	0	1	1	2	2	3	3	4	4
91	9590	9595	9600	9605	9609	9614	9619	9624	9628	9633	0	1	1	2	2	3	3	4	4
92	9638	9643	9647	9652	9657	9661	9666	9671	9675	9680	0	1	1	2	2	3	3	4	4
93	9685	9689	9694	9699	9703	9708	9713	9717	9722	9727	0	1	1	2	2	3	3	4	4
94	9731	9736	9741	9745	9750	9754	9759	9763	9768	9773	0	1	1	2	2	3	3	4	4
95	9777	9782	9786	9791	9795	9800	9805	9809	9814	9818	0	1	1	2	2	3	3	4	4
96	9823	9827	9832	9836	9841	9845	9850	9854	9859	9863	0	1	1	2	2	3	3	4	4
97	9868	9872	9877	9881	9886	9890	9894	9899	9903	9908	0	1	1	2	2	3	3	4	4
98	9912	9917	9921	9926	9930	9934	9939	9943	9948	9952	0	1	1	2	2	3	3	4	4
99	9956	9961	9965	9969	9974	9978	9983	9987	9991	9996	0	1	1	2	2	3	3	3	4

TABLE 14

ATOMIC WEIGHTS OF THE MORE COMMON ELEMENTS

	Symbol	Atomic Weight		Symbol	Atomic Weight
Aluminium........	Al	27.0	Manganese.......	Mn	54.9
Antimony.........	Sb	120.2	Mercury.........	Hg	200.6
Arsenic............	As	75.0	Nickel...........	Ni	58.7
Barium...........	Ba	137.4	Nitrogen.........	N	14.0
Bismuth..........	Bi	209.0	Oxygen..........	O	16.0
Boron.............	B	10.9	Phosphorus.......	P	31.0
Bromine...........	Br	79.9	Platinum.........	Pt	195.2
Cadmium.........	Cd	112.4	Potassium........	K	39.1
Calcium...........	Ca	40.1	Radium..........	Ra	220.0
Carbon............	C	12.0	Selenium.........	Se	79.2
Chlorine...........	Cl	35.5	Silicon...........	Si	28.1
Chromium.........	Cr	52.0	Silver............	Ag	107.9
Cobalt............	Co	59.0	Sodium..........	Na	23.0
Copper............	Cu	63.6	Strontium........	Sr	87.6
Fluorine...........	F	19.0	Sulphur..........	S	32.1
Gold..............	Au	197.2	Tellurium........	Te	127.5
Helium............	He	4.0	Tin..............	Sn	118.7
Hydrogen.........	H	1.0	Titanium.........	Ti	48.1
Iodine............	I	126.9	Tungsten.........	W	184.0
Iron.............	Fe	55.8	Uranium.........	U	238.2
Lead..............	Pb	207.2	Vanadium........	V	51.0
Lithium...........	Li	6.9	Zinc.............	Zn	65.4
Magnesium.......	Mg	24.3	Zirconium........	Zr	90.6

TABLE 15

VALUES OF F FOR DROP-WEIGHT METHOD OF

DETERMINING SURFACE TENSION

(Harkins and Brown)

$\dfrac{r}{V^{\frac{1}{3}}}$	F	$\dfrac{r}{V^{\frac{1}{3}}}$	F
0.00	(1.0000)	0.85	0.5992
0.30	0.7256	0.90	0.5998
0.35	0.7011	0.95	0.6034
0.40	0.6828	1.00	0.6098
0.45	0.6669	1.05	0.6179
0.50	0.6515	1.10	0.6280
0.55	0.6362	1.15	0.6407
0.60	0.6250	1.20	0.6535
0.65	0.6171	1.225	(0.6555)
0.70	0.6093	1.25	(0.6521)
0.75	0.6032	1.30	(0.6401)
0.80	0.6000		

TABLE 16

ABSOLUTE VISCOSITY OF WATER AT VARIOUS

TEMPERATURES (in Poises)

(After Hosking)

Temperature, Degrees	Absolute Viscosity	Temperature, Degrees	Absolute Viscosity
0	0.0179	40	0.0066
5	0.0152	50	0.0055
10	0.0131	60	0.0047
15	0.0114	70	0.0041
20	0.0101	80	0.0036
25	0.0089	90	0.0032
30	0.0080	100	0.0028

TABLE 17

Buffer Solutions

McIlvaine's standards

pH	0.2 M Na_2HPO_4	0.1 M Citric Acid	pH	0.2 M Na_2HPO_4	0.1 M Citric Acid
	c.c.	c.c.		c.c.	c.c.
2.2	0.40	19.60	5.2	10.72	9.28
2.4	1.24	18.76	5.4	11.15	8.85
2.6	2.18	17.82	5.6	11.60	8.40
2.8	3.17	16.83	5.8	12.09	7.91
3.0	4.11	15.89	6.0	12.63	7.37
3.2	4.94	15.06	6.2	13.22	6.78
3.4	5.70	14.30	6.4	13.85	6.15
3.6	6.44	13.56	6.6	14.55	5.45
3.8	7.10	12.90	6.8	15.45	4.55
4.0	7.71	12.29	7.0	16.47	3.53
4.2	8.28	11.72	7.2	17.39	2.61
4.4	8.82	11.18	7.4	18.17	1.83
4.6	9.35	10.65	7.6	18.73	1.27
4.8	9.86	10.14	7.8	19.15	0.85
5.0	10.30	9.70	8.0	19.45	0.55

Sørensen Standards

Borate: 12.404 g. H_3BO_3 + 100 c.c. N NaOH per liter   HCl: Tenth normal

pH	c.c. Borate	c.c. HCl	pH	c.c. Borate	c.c. HCl
7.61	5.25	4.75	8.79	7.5	2.5
7.93	5.5	4.5	8.89	8.0	2.0
8.13	5.75	4.25	8.99	8.5	1.5
8.27	6.0	4.0	9.15	9.5	0.5
8.49	6.5	3.5	9.23	10.0	0.0
8.67	7.0	3.0			

TABLE 17—*Continued*

BUFFER SOLUTIONS

Kolthoff and Vleeschhouwer Standards

Solution A: 5.30 gms. Na_2CO_3 per liter
Solution B: 19.10 gms. $Na_2B_4O_7 \cdot 10H_2O$ per liter

pH	Sol. A	Sol. B	pH	Sol. A	Sol. B
9.2	0.0	100.0	10.2	82.15	17.85
9.4	35.7	64.3	10.4	89.6	13.1
9.6	55.5	44.5	10.6	91.5	8.5
9.8	66.7	33.3	10.8	94.75	5.25
10.0	75.4	24.6	11.0	97.3	2.7

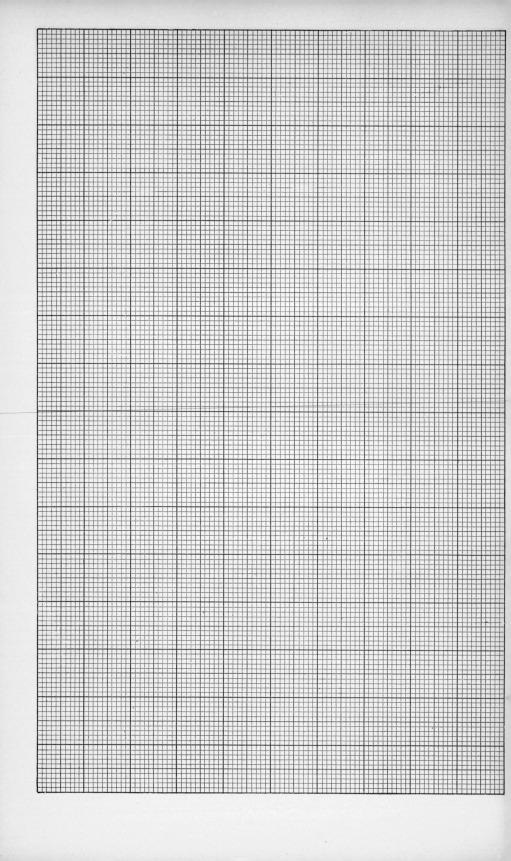

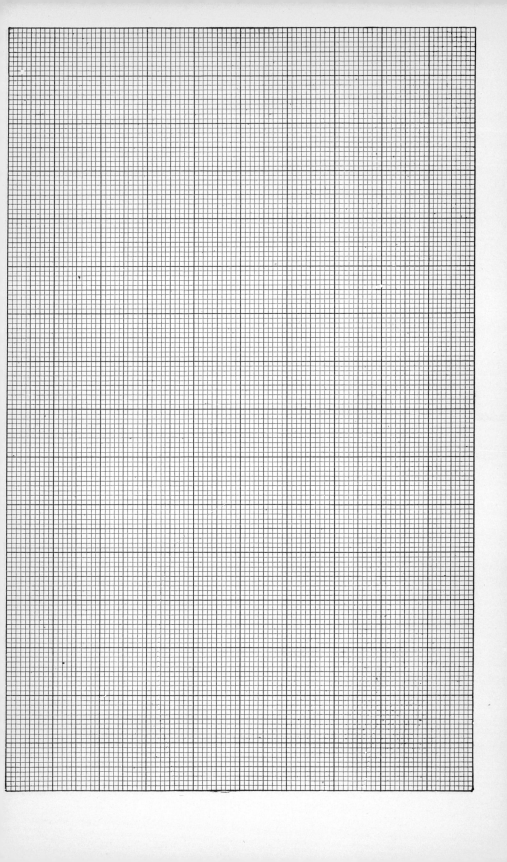

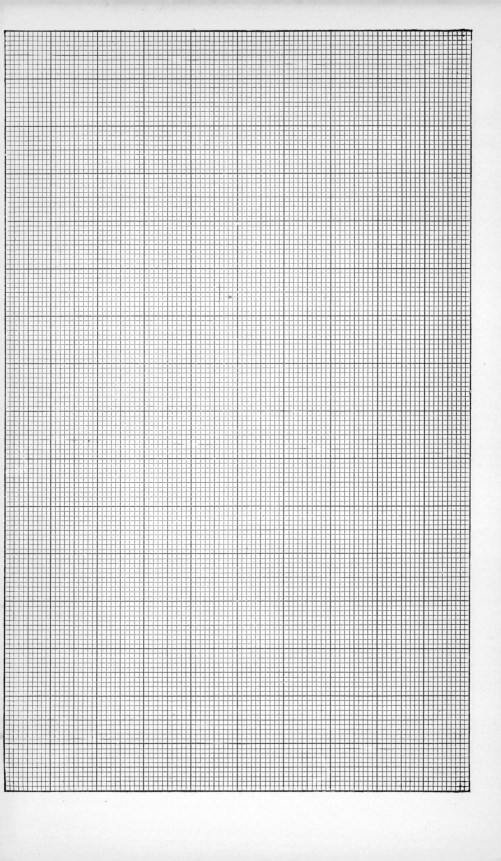